Please Return to:

Suzanne Lyons

Mountain View - Los Altos Union
High School District

TEXTBOOK No. **318**

Student's Name	Date Issued

S0-BCO-417

fth Edition

Introductory
Physical Science

Haber-Schaim | Gerald L. Abegg | John H. Dodge | H. Graden Kirksey | James A. Walter

ntice-Hall, Inc., Englewood Cliffs, New Jersey 07632

Introductory Physical Science

Fifth Edition

Uri Haber-Schaim | Gerald L. Abegg | John H. Dodge | H. Graden Kirksey | James A. Walter

© 1987, 1982, 1977, by Uri Haber-Schaim; © 1972 by Newton College of the Sacred Heart. Copyright assigned to Uri Haber-Schaim, 1974; © 1967 by Education Development Center, Inc. Published by Prentice-Hall, Inc., Englewood Cliffs, New Jersey 07632. All rights reserved. No part of this book may be reproduced in any form or by any means without permission in writing from the publisher. This edition of *Introductory Physical Science* is a revision under free licensing of the work under the same title copyrighted originally by Education Development Center, Inc. The publication does not imply approval or disapproval by the original copyright holder.

Printed in the United States of America.

ISBN 0-13-502840-0 Cloth

ISBN 0-13-502857-4 Paper

IPS Teacher's Guide and Resource Book   ISBN 0-13-502865-5
IPS Notebook   ISBN 0-13-502873-6

10   9   8   7   6

Prentice-Hall of Australia, Pty. Ltd., Sydney
Prentice-Hall Canada Inc., Toronto
Prentice-Hall Hispanoamericana, S.A., Mexico
Prentice-Hall of India Private Ltd., New Delhi
Prentice-Hall International (UK) Ltd., London
Prentice-Hall of Japan, Inc., Tokyo
Prentice-Hall of Southeast Asia Pte. Ltd., Singapore
Editora Prentice Hall do Brasil Ltda., Rio de Janeiro
Whitehall Books Limited, Wellington, New Zealand

Preface to the Fifth Edition

The fifth edition of *IPS* contains two new chapters: Chapter 9, Electric Charge; and Chapter 10, Atoms and Electric Charge. However, users have the option of skipping these chapters and proceeding directly to either Chapter 11, Sizes and Masses of Atoms and Molecules, or Chapter 12, Molecular Motion (Chapters 10 and 9 in the fourth edition). Thus, this edition presents additional material for faster classes and offers new options for slower classes.

Specifically, the option of ending the course with Chapters 9 and 10 reinforces an understanding of the laws of constant and multiple proportions. Yet this option eliminates the need for Experiment 8.7: Two Compounds of Copper, one of the hardest and longest experiments in the course. The option of going directly from Chapter 8 to Chapter 12, to which a discussion of Brownian motion has been added, ties Chapter 12 more strongly to the revised Chapter 7, by highlighting the common properties of the random events of radioactive decay and molecular motion. Neither of these options requires the use of arithmetic with powers of ten.

To strengthen the preparation for chemistry, a discussion of relative atomic masses and the mole has been added to Chapter 8. Further minor changes, both additions and deletions, have been made throughout Chapters 7–12.

A new feature to be found at the end of Chapters 1–12 consists of suggested "Themes for Short Essays." The purpose of this new kind of assignment is to encourage the use of imagination to integrate classroom experience with the outside world, real or fictional.

The basic purpose of the course has not changed. The program seeks to give all students a beginning knowledge of physical science and to offer insight into the means by which scientific knowledge is acquired.

The *IPS* course helps students to understand some of the basic principles of physical science and to acquire useful laboratory skills; it also encourages the exercise of reasoning skills. The course further provides an opportunity for students to develop their ability to communicate by requiring the individual student to take part in a collective learning process. *IPS* students learn from nature, the text, their teachers, and each other.

The theme of the course is the development of evidence for an atomic model of matter. Rather than broadly surveying the entire field of physical science, we have taken a well-defined path toward this major objective. The method employed to achieve the stated goals is one of experimentation and guided reasoning based on the results of student experiments. Thus the body of the text includes laboratory experiments which students must carry out to understand the course properly. Many of the conclusions and generalizations arrived at and recorded in the student laboratory notebook complement the text in an essential way.

Although laboratory space is always an asset, the experiments in this course have been successfully performed in classrooms containing individual flat desk tops and one sink.

Chapters 9 and 10 were adapted from *Energy, A Sequel to IPS.* Classes continuing with *Energy* can go directly to Chapter 14, with only a minor supplement from Chapter 13 at a later time.

We are indebted to the many persons who contributed to the development of this material in the early stages. We are also indebted to the many *IPS* teachers, especially Workshop instructors, who provide us with constant assessment of the program.

March 1986

Uri Haber-Schaim

Gerald L. Abegg

John H. Dodge

H. Graden Kirksey

James A. Walter†

---

†Our friend and colleague James A. Walter passed away after the completion of the manuscript, while the book was in production.

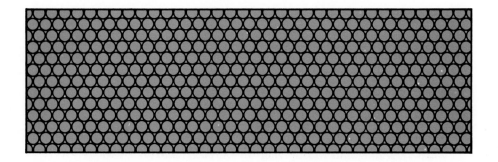

Contents

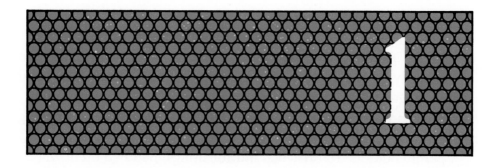

Introduction

Look around you. Note the almost endless variety of substances and forms. There are concrete walls, wooden desks, glass windows, and metal pipes. Outside there are trees, clouds, and perhaps rivers with fish in them. We can make the list as long as we wish.

We can invent schemes that explain the endless variety of material things in terms of fewer, simpler things. Many different things could conceivably be made from the same units by putting them together in a variety of ways. For example, we can use bricks in many ways—to make a wall or a house or a doorstop or a paved street. Over 2,000 years ago, the Greek philosopher Democritus conceived of small units, which he called "atoms." But Democritus did not really know that there *were* atoms or how many different kinds there were. His ideas must have been important, because we still use the word "atom"; but the word in itself does not really explain anything. It did not help people to predict any properties of matter or to understand what kind of changes could take place.

Modern chemistry and physics can give a much more meaningful account of the properties of matter. If this account is to have any meaning for you, we shall have to start at the beginning. We cannot just throw new words at you. Each step must be filled in with many experiments that you will perform. Then all the words and ideas will correspond to something real for you, and you will reach conclusions on your own.

13

You have been using this process—consciously or unconsciously—throughout your life. When you were a baby, signals from the outside world poured into you through your senses, but they had little meaning for you. You had to learn their meaning by physically reacting to your environment—that is, you learned by experimentation. You reached out for things, handled them when you could, threw them about. These early activities gave you a sense of size, of location, of weight. You began to associate the properties of objects with their appearance, so that you could begin to know something about objects through seeing them without having to handle them.

By the time you were two or three years old, signals from the outside world had acquired meaning for you. Particularly, you had learned to understand your parents' talk, and you had begun to talk yourself. After that, how rapidly your learning accelerated! By asking questions and understanding answers, you could learn from other persons' experiences in addition to your own.

As time has gone on, you have continued to learn by experimenting and by asking questions and seeking answers. You cannot learn to ride a bicycle without getting on one. But it certainly helps to have a friend who already knows how to ride.

So the study of science is really only a continuation of the activities that you have done many times before. In this course, you will be concerned chiefly with how to ask questions of nature and how to carry out experiments that will help you find some answers.

Let us first list some of the properties of matter that we can observe. Then we shall select a few of these properties and learn how to measure them and how to use them to distinguish between different materials. Finally we shall use them to put some real meaning into the word "atom."

Here is a list of questions that relate to some of the properties in which substances differ. Can you answer them?

A substance can be a solid, a liquid, or a gas. Are ice and water the same substance? What do you mean by substance?

A substance can have a high boiling point or a low boiling point. What substances have higher boiling points than water?

A substance can be more or less dense than another substance. What does this mean?

A substance can be an insulator or a conductor of electricity;

a substance can be either brittle or malleable. Is there any connection between brittleness and electrical conductivity?

A substance can be strong or weak. Which is stronger, aluminum or copper? What do you mean by strong?

When you heat something, does its temperature always rise?

Some substances are more soluble than others in water or in alcohol. How can solubility be measured?

One of the best ways to find out how a thing works—and what it is made of—is to take it apart. Sometimes you can even test your understanding of it by trying to put it together again. But, of course, it matters how you take it apart. If you hit a watch with a hammer, it will certainly come apart, but you will not learn much about how it works; and you certainly cannot put it back together. A great deal of modern experimental science is involved in learning how to take things apart in some instructive fashion. (Of course, we have to learn about some things, such as stars, without being able to get at them.)

We shall start illustrating this way of learning about matter by taking something apart. We have chosen a common form of matter, one that separates into many different substances when heated—namely, wood. The things you do when you take wood apart by heating and the questions that will come up will serve as our starting point.

1.1 EXPERIMENT   DISTILLATION OF WOOD

What will happen if you heat some wood splints in a test tube without burning them? Try to predict what will happen before you read on.

Pack a Pyrex test tube with wood splints, and connect it to the apparatus as shown in Figure 1.1. After your teacher has checked your setup, heat the tube strongly with the two burners. **CAUTION:** Wear safety glasses whenever you are heating something or working with gases.

- What do you observe happening when it gets hot?

- Will the gas that comes out of the tube burn? Try lighting it.

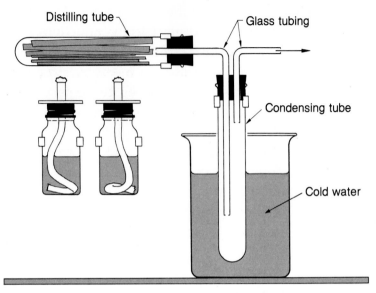

Figure 1.1
Apparatus used in distilling wood. Lubricate the glass tubing with glycerine or water before pushing it into the stoppers. Hold the tubing with a towel as close to the stopper as possible while pushing it in. This will prevent the tubing from hurting you in case it breaks.

Figure 1.2
Apparatus for collecting gas from the distillation of wood. The gas collects over water in the water-filled bottle on the right. The bucket should be about one-third full of water.

Now attach a rubber tube to the apparatus, and collect the gas in a bottle by the displacement of water (Figure 1.2). When the bottle is full of gas, disconnect the rubber tube, relight the gas coming from the test tube, and keep it burning as long as you can. As the gas may come out in puffs, you may have to relight it frequently. You probably will have to tilt or move the burners to heat all the wood.

Examine the liquid in the upright test tube.

- Is it one liquid or more than one?

Disconnect the tube containing the condensed liquid, and put in a few pieces of broken porcelain. Connect the apparatus as shown in Figure 1.3, and boil off about half of the liquid. The porcelain chips keep the liquid boiling evenly.

- What happens?

Figure 1.3
Apparatus for obtaining more information about the distillation of wood. The burner-stand screen reduces the amount of heat reaching the test tube and keeps the liquid from boiling too rapidly.

- Is the liquid that condensed in the right-hand test tube the same as that in the left-hand one?

- What happens if you mix them together?

After the test tube containing the wood has cooled, examine the remains of the wood splints. Try burning one.

- Does it leave any ash?

- Could you predict, just by looking at and handling the wood, that all these gases and liquids can be obtained from it?

- Can you get the wood back by mixing all the material you have collected?

- Were these substances there all the time, or were they formed by heating? Have you any evidence for your answer?

- How can you compare the amounts of the different solids, liquids, and gases that you got from the wood?

In order to get more definite answers to these questions, we shall do experiments, and these in turn will raise new questions. We shall start in the next chapter with the question: How can we compare amounts of solids, liquids, and gases?

 **Themes for Short Essays**

1 You have burned a wooden match and heated wood in a closed test tube. Certainly you noticed that at least two entirely different things happen to wood when it is heated strongly under different conditions. Is heating wood a special case or does the outcome of any process depend upon the conditions under which it takes place? Write an essay on this question using everyday activities as examples of processes.

2 Write a letter to a friend in which you expand on the discussion you had in class on the questions "Are ice and water the same substance? What do you mean by a substance?"

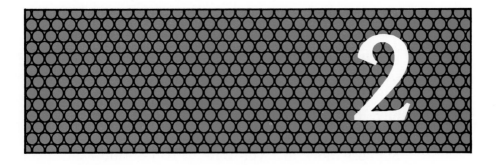

Volume and Mass

2.1 VOLUME

Suppose that you have some pennies stacked one on top of another in several piles, and that you want to know how many pennies are in each pile. The obvious thing to do is to count them. If you had to count the pennies in many piles, you could speed up the counting in the following way: Make a scale like that shown in Figure 2.1, marking it off in spaces equal to the thickness of one penny. You can then place this scale alongside each pile and read off the number of pennies.

Figure 2.1
A scale for counting the number of pennies in a vertical pile. The distance between marks is the thickness of one penny.

If you want to measure the amount of copper in each pile of pennies, you first have to decide in which unit to measure the amount of copper. If you choose as the unit the amount of copper in one penny, then the amount in the whole pile is expressed by the same number as the number of pennies.

Suppose, now, that you want to find out how much copper there is in a solid rectangular bar of copper. You might think of making a box of the same size and shape as the copper bar and then counting the number of pennies needed to fill the box. This idea will not work, because if you place pennies next to one another in a rectangular box, there will always be some empty space between them.

A better way to measure the amount of copper in the bar is to choose a new unit, such as the volume of a small cube. Suppose

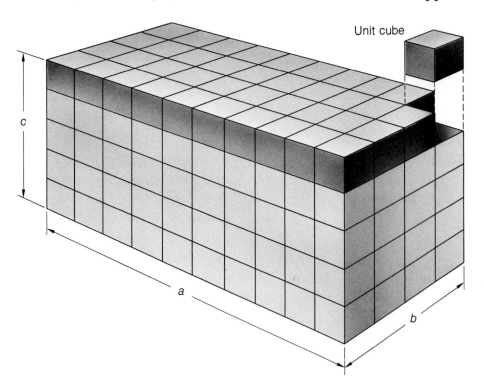

Figure 2.2
A bar of copper 10 cubes long, 4 cubes wide, and 5 cubes high. One layer of the bar contains 10 rows of 4 cubes each, or 10×4 cubes. We see that there are 5 layers in the bar, each containing 10×4 cubes. The total number of unit cubes in the bar is therefore $10 \times 4 \times 5 = 200$ cubes. If the unit cube is 1 cm on an edge, the volume of the bar is 200 cm^3 (cubic centimeters). For any rectangular solid, therefore, the volume is the product of the three dimensions, $a \times b \times c$.

we had a box the same size and shape as the copper bar, and we could fill it with cubes of copper of a size that would fit without air spaces between them. We could simply count the number of cubes to find the amount. Of course, we do not have to count each cube. If *a* cubes fit along the length of the box, *b* along the width, and *c* along the height, then the total number of cubes in the box (and bar) is $a \times b \times c$. (See Figure 2.2.) This is the amount of copper in the solid bar, expressed in units of cubes. As you probably know, this is also the *volume* of the bar, expressed in terms of the volume of the unit cube.

What we choose to be the length of each side of this unit cube is a matter of convenience. We shall choose a unit of length based on the meter (m), the international standard of the metric system. In this case, as in much of our work in this course, we shall use the centimeter (cm). A centimeter is $\frac{1}{100}$ m. Our unit cube would then be the cubic centimeter (cm³), a small cube 1 cm on an edge.

To sum up, then, we can compare different amounts of the same substance by comparing their volumes—that is, the amounts of space they occupy. When we are dealing with a rectangular solid, we find its volume by measuring its three edges and taking the product of these numbers. We can also calculate the volumes of solids of other regular shapes from measurements of their dimensions, but this requires further knowledge of geometry.

The use of volume to compare amounts of substances is particularly convenient when we deal with liquids, because liquids take the shape of their containers. If we wish to compare the amounts of water contained in two bottles of very

Figure 2.3
A graduated cylinder marked off in units of volume. The cubic-centimeter marks could be made by filling the cylinder with liquid from a small cubic container, 1 cm on an edge, and making a mark at the liquid level each time a containerful of the liquid is poured in. Many graduated cylinders are marked off in milliliters (ml). A milliliter is the same as a cubic centimeter.

different shapes, we simply pour the contents of each separately into a graduated cylinder that has already been marked off with the desired units; we then read off the volumes (Figure 2.3). This way of measuring volume is very much like counting pennies all stacked up in a pile.

We can use the property of a liquid to take any shape when we want to find the volume of a solid of irregular shape, such as a small stone. After pouring some water into a graduated cylinder and reading its volume, we can submerge the stone in the water and read the combined volume of the water and the stone. The difference between the two readings is the volume of the stone.

1† A student has a large number of cubes that measure 1 cm along an edge. If you find it helpful, use a drawing or a set of cubes to answer the following questions.
a) How many cubes will be needed to build a cube that is 2 cm along an edge?
b) How many cubes will be needed to build a cube that is 3 cm along an edge?
c) Express, in cubic centimeters, the volumes of the cubes built in (a) and (b).

2   One rectangular box is 30 cm long, 15 cm wide, and 10 cm deep. A second rectangular box is 25 cm long, 16 cm wide, and 15 cm deep. Which box has the larger volume?

3   Figure A shows a cone-shaped graduate used for measuring the volume of liquids. Why are the divisions not equally spaced?

Figure A
For problem 3

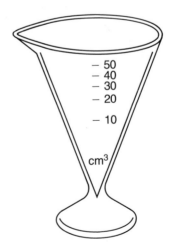

2.2 READING SCALES

To measure length with a ruler, volume with a graduated cylinder, and temperature with a thermometer, you must be able to read a scale. Therefore, learning how to get all the information a scale can provide is a useful skill.

We shall begin with reading a metric ruler (Figure 2.4). The smallest divisions on such a ruler are 0.1 cm (1 mm) apart. This is a small distance indeed. Nevertheless, when the object you wish to measure has sharp edges, you can see whether the edge falls on one of the lines.

In Figure 2.5, the edge falls between two lines. It is clear that the length is between 4.8 cm and 4.9 cm. To gain more information, estimate the position of the edge. If you cannot tell whether the edge is closer to one line or the other, it is best to report the reading as 4.85 cm, or 48.5 mm.

If the edge is closer to the left line, report the reading as 4.82 cm or 4.83 cm. Either way, you will not be off by more than ±0.02 cm. (The notation ± means "plus or minus.") Similarly, if you decide that the edge is closer to the right line, report the reading as 4.87 cm or 4.88 cm. Again, you will not be off by more than ±0.02 cm. Had you read the scale as 4.8 cm or 4.9 cm, you might have been off by as much as 0.05 cm.

Figure 2.4
A metric ruler. The numbered divisions are centimeters; the small divisions are $\frac{1}{10}$ cm, or millimeters.

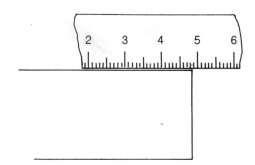

Figure 2.5
Reading the position of the edge of an object. Here the edge falls between two of the millimeter marks.

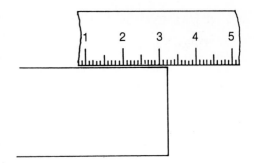

Figure 2.6
Reading the position of the edge of
an object. Here the edge falls on one
of the millimeter marks.

Suppose that, as far as you can tell, the edge falls on a line
(Figure 2.6). Then you should report the reading as 3.20 cm. This
will indicate that the reading is closer to 3.20 cm than to either 3.22
cm or 3.18 cm. Here the "0" gives us information that would be lost
had you written only 3.2 cm.

---

4 The scale in Figure B is in centimeters. Estimate the positions of arrows *a* and *b* to the nearest 0.1 cm. Can you estimate their positions to
0.01 cm? To 0.001 cm?

Figure B
For problem 4

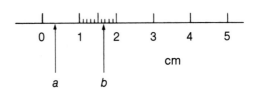

5† What fractions of a cubic centimeter do the smallest divisions on
each of the graduated cylinders in Figure C represent?

Figure C
For problem 5

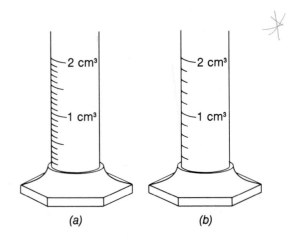

Figure D
For problem 6

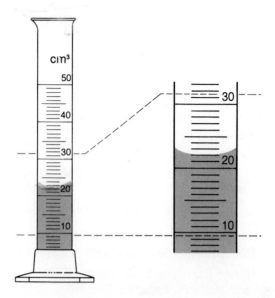

6　A close look at Figure D shows that the top of the liquid contained in the graduated cylinder is not flat but curved. How do you decide how much water is in the cylinder?

7　Three students reported the length of a pencil to be 12 cm, 12.0 cm, and 12.00 cm. Do all three readings contain the same information?

8　What advantage is there to making graduated cylinders narrow and tall rather than short and wide?

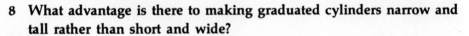

2.3　EXPERIMENT　MEASURING VOLUME
BY DISPLACEMENT OF WATER

A granular solid like sand, although it does not flow as well as a liquid, can be measured by the same method. Suppose we have some sand in a cup. We can find how much space it takes up in the cup by simply pouring it into a graduated cylinder. But does the mark it comes to on the scale of the cylinder really show the volume of the sand? What about the air spaces between the loosely packed grains? The graduated cylinder really measures the combined volume of the sand plus the air spaces. However, we can do a simple experiment to find the volume of the sand alone.

　　Pour some sand into a dry graduated cylinder until it is about two-thirds full.

●　What is the volume reading on the scale?

Now pour the sand into a beaker, and pour water into the graduated cylinder until it is about one-third full. Record the volume of the water, and then add the sand to the water.

- What is the volume of sand plus water?

- What is the volume of the sand alone?

- What is the volume of the air space in the sand?

- What fraction of the dry sand is just air space?

The experiment you have just done shows that we must be careful when we talk about the volume of a sample of a dry substance like sand. We must say how the volume was measured. If we

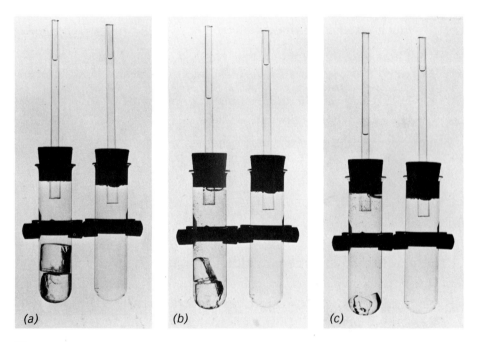

(a)   (b)   (c)

Figure 2.7

(a) A test tube containing only water and another test tube containing water to which two large pieces of rock salt have just been added. (b) The same test tubes 30 minutes later, after the salt has begun to dissolve. Notice the decrease in the total volume of the rock salt and water, as shown by the water level in the narrow glass tube. The test tube containing the salt was shaken several times to speed up the dissolving. (c) The test tubes after another 30 minutes. The total volume continues to decrease as more salt dissolves.

have a bag of dry sand and want to know how many quart bottles it will fill, we need to know its volume dry. But if we want to know the volume of sand alone, not sand plus air space, then we must do an experiment like the one you have just done. We must measure the volume by liquid displacement.

Whenever we measure the volume of a solid by displacement of water, we make the assumption that the volumes of the solid alone and of the water alone add up to the volume of the solid and water together. This assumption may or may not be correct. This will depend on the kind of solid we have. For example, if you measure the volume of a few chunks of rock salt by the displacement of water, you will see that the total volume of rock salt and water becomes less as the salt dissolves. (See Figure 2.7.)

9† A volume of 50 cm^3 of dry sand is added to 30 cm^3 of water for a total volume of 60 cm^3.
a)   What is the volume of water that does *not* go into air spaces between the sand particles?
b)   What is the volume of water that does fill air spaces between the sand particles?
c)   What is the volume of the air spaces between the particles in the dry sand?
d)   What is the volume of the sand particles alone?
e)   What fraction of the total volume of the dry sand is sand particles?

10   How would you measure the volume of granulated sugar?

11   How would you measure the volume of a cork stopper?

2.4   SHORTCOMINGS OF VOLUME AS A MEASURE OF MATTER

The experiment shown in Figure 2.7 strongly suggests that volume is not always a good measure of the amount of a substance. Here are some other difficulties: Suppose you wanted to find the amount of gas given off in your distillation of wood. You could measure the volume of gas you produced by filling bottles (displacing the water in them) until no more gas was left. You could thus use one bottle as a unit of volume and express the volume as so many bottles of gas. Or you could collect the gas in inverted water-filled graduated cylinders instead of bottles and express the volume in cubic centimeters.

But if you have ever pumped up a bicycle tire with air, you know that a gas is very compressible. You know that, as you push more and more gas into the tire, its volume remains almost unchanged. Does this mean that the amount of gas in the tire remains almost unchanged, too? If you compressed the gas obtained from the distillation of wood into a smaller volume, would there be less of it?

Finally, can we really use volume to compare the amounts of different substances, some of which may be solids, some liquids, and others gases? Consider again the distillation of wood. Does measuring the volume of the wood splints, the ashes, the liquids, and the gas really tell us how much of each of these substances we have?

2.5   MASS

The limitations of volume as a measure of the amount of matter must have been known to people many centuries ago because they developed a method for measuring the amounts of different substances independently of their volumes. From an Egyptian tomb several thousand years old, archaeologists have recovered a little balance arm of carved stone, with carefully made stone masses (Figure 2.8). It was almost surely used, in the very dawn of history, for the careful measurement of gold dust. Goldsmiths knew even then that the balance was the best way to determine the amount of solid gold they could get from any heap of dust or from any pile of irregularly shaped nuggets.

The balance was hung by the upper loop so that the horizontal bar was divided exactly into two arms of equal length. With no objects suspended from either arm, the balance bar would hang horizontally. When an object was hung from the loop on the end of one arm, it could be balanced by hanging some other objects from the end of the other arm.

No doubt, in using the balance, people soon learned that the bar would remain horizontal even though there were drastic changes in the shapes of the objects being balanced. Dividing a

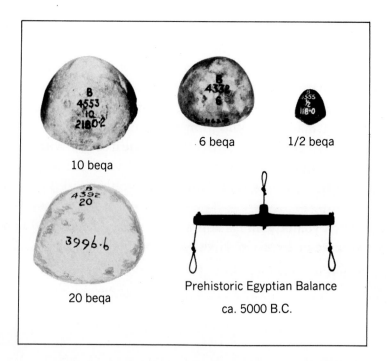

Figure 2.8
This balance, the earliest one known, comes from a prehistoric grave at Naqada, Egypt, and may be 7,000 years old. It uses limestone masses and has a red limestone beam which is 8.5 cm long. (The limestone masses and beam are not shown to the same scale.) Other limestone masses of different numbers of *beqa* (BEK-ah) were also found in these prehistoric graves. Is there any reason why you should not use the *beqa* as your unit of mass? *(Courtesy of Science Museum, London)*

chunk of iron into a number of pieces or filing it into a pile of small grains does not affect the balance. A balance responds to something quite independent of the form of the object. What it responds to we call "mass."

Suppose a piece of gold balances a piece of wood, and the piece of wood balances a piece of brass. Then we say that the masses of all three are equal. If something else balances the piece of brass, it also balances the wood and the gold and therefore has the same mass. The equal-arm balance gives us a way of comparing masses of objects of any kind, regardless of their shape, form, color, or what substance they are made of.

To record masses, we shall need some standard masses with which various other pieces of matter can be compared. This standard mass is arbitrary—any mass, even the ancient Egyptian *beqa*, can be chosen—but people must agree on it. In our work we shall use the gram (g), the fundamental unit of mass in the metric system. The international standard of mass in the metric system is a carefully made cylinder of platinum kept at Sèvres, near Paris, France, that has a mass of 1 kilogram (kg), or 1,000 g. All other kilogram masses are compared, directly or indirectly, with the standard whenever high precision is required. If we were to place a mass of 1 kg on the grocer's scale, the scale would read 2.2 pounds.

---

12   **When you buy things at the store, are they measured more often by volume or by mass? Give some examples.**

13   **What is your mass in kg?**

2.6 EXPERIMENT   THE EQUAL-ARM BALANCE

In later experiments, you will often use an equal-arm balance. The purpose of this experiment is to make you familiar with it and to allow you to develop the necessary skill in using it (Figure 2.9).

Figure 2.9
An equal-arm laboratory balance like the one you will use in your experiments. The object to be massed is placed on the pan at the left, and the standard gram masses are placed on the one at the right. The tip of the pointer hangs vertically down over the scale in the middle of the base.

Make sure that the pans swing freely and that the vertical pointer in the center does not rub against the support. The pointer of the balance should swing very nearly the same distance on each side of the center of the scale when there is nothing on either pan. In order to adjust the balance so that it swings in this manner, first make sure that the pointed metal rider on the right arm is as near to the center of the balance as possible. Then move the rider on the left arm until the long pointer on the center of the balance swings the same distance on each side of the center of the scale on the bottom of the balance.

Your balance comes with a set of masses, the smallest of which is 100 mg (1 mg, a milligram, is equal to 0.001 g. Thus 100 mg = 0.100 g). Now that your balance is adjusted, use a set of gram masses to mass several objects of between 1 and 20 grams. (We shall abbreviate "to find the mass of" to the verb "to mass.")

Exchange objects with your classmates, and compare your measurements with theirs. Do not divulge your measurements until all students have recorded their measurements.

2.7 EXPERIMENT   CALIBRATING THE BALANCE

Look carefully at several pennies. Do you think they all have the same mass? Would you expect them to differ a little in mass? Now measure the masses of the pennies on your balance. Record the mass of each penny in a table in your notebook, and be careful to keep track of which penny is which.

You have massed the pennies only to the nearest 0.1 g. How can they be massed to less than 0.1 g to see if there are tiny differences in their masses, smaller than 0.1 g? By using the rider on the right arm of the balance, you can measure masses to less than 0.1 g. Move the rider until it balances a 0.1-g mass placed on the left-hand pan, and mark its position on the arm. Now make pencil marks on the arm, dividing into 10 equal spaces the distance between the 0-g and the 0.1-g position of the rider. Each mark represents an interval of 0.01 g on this rider scale.

- How can you check to see if this is true?

If your balance has already been calibrated (that is, if there already is a scale marked on it), check to see if it is accurate.

2.8 EXPERIMENT   THE PRECISION OF THE BALANCE

Now that you have calibrated your balance, again measure the mass of each penny.

- How do the masses of the pennies compare?

- How much more precise is the balance when you use the rider than it was without a rider?

Since the space between the 0.01-g marks could also be divided into 10 equal spaces, does this mean that the balance masses accurately to 0.001 g (or 1 mg)?

To find out, mass a light object and a heavy object separately to the nearest 0.001 g. Make these massings several times, alternating light and heavy so that the balance must be readjusted for each massing. You do not have to wait for the balance to come to rest. It is necessary only that the pointer swing equal distances to the right and left of the center.

- What do you conclude?

14† Karen massed an object three different times, using the same balance and gram masses. Her results were: 18.324 g, 18.308 g, and 18.342 g. How could she best report the mass of the object?

15 Aram masses an object on his balance. By mistake he places the object in the pan on the same side as the rider. He balances the object by means of 4.500 g in the opposite pan and by setting the rider to 0.060 g. What is the mass of the object?

16 Five students in turn used the same balance to measure the mass of a small dish; none knew what results the others obtained. The masses they found were

Student	Mass (g)
1	3.752
2	3.755
3	3.752
4	3.756
5	3.760

a) Can you tell whether any student made an incorrect measurement?

b) Do you think there is anything wrong with the balance?

c) What do you think would be the best way to report the mass of the dish?

d) How precise do you think the measurements were?

17 An equal-arm balance good to 0.01 g is used to mass two objects. If their masses are measured as 0.10 g and 4.00 g, what is the expected percentage error of each measurement?

18 You were told that your balance is an equal-arm balance, but suppose that the right arm is longer than the left arm. Would the object that is massed on your balance appear to have a mass that is greater than, less than, or the same as, its true mass?

2.9 AN UNEQUAL-ARM BALANCE: MASSING A TRUCK

When you calibrated your equal-arm balance, you placed a 0.1-g mass on the left pan, then moved the rider on the right-hand arm out until it balanced the 0.1-g mass. You marked the location of the rider, then divided the part of the arm between the rider and its zero position into ten parts. When you moved the rider to the 0.05 mark, it balanced a mass of 0.05 g. You learned that moving the rider farther in allowed it to balance a smaller mass.

Suppose we have a beam like the arms of the balance, with a pan on one end and a rider near the other. By trial, we can find a

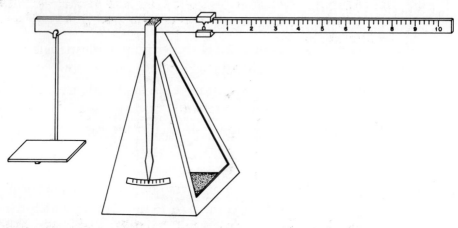

Figure 2.10
An unequal-arm balance with one rider.

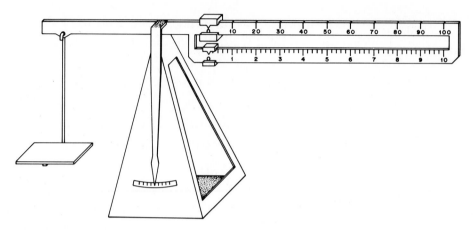

Figure 2.11
An unequal-arm balance with two riders of different mass.

location where the beam can be balanced with the rider moved to a position near the supporting wedge, as shown in Figure 2.10. We mark this position of the rider zero. Suppose we add some object of known mass to the pan. We find that we have to move the rider out to a new location to have the beam balanced again. We mark this new position. If we add a second object of the same mass to the pan, we must move the rider farther out to balance the objects, and we make another mark. We continue to do this until the rider can go no farther. We find our marks have been made at equal intervals, and we can label them with the masses of the objects we placed on the pan.

Thus we can use a rider to measure the masses of heavier objects. We can even make our balance with a double arm on the right, having riders of two different sizes. This increases the precision of the balance (Figure 2.11). Such unequal-arm balances are very common. You probably have stood on one in your physician's office or in your school's health office. In such balances, the "arm" of the balance is not a single bar but is made of several parts. However, the principle is the same as it was in the case of the rider of your laboratory balance.

A more impressive unequal-arm balance is the kind used for massing trucks (Figure 2.12). The "arm" on which the platform with the truck rests is very short compared to the arm on which the two riders rest (Figure 2.13).

Figure 2.12
A trailer truck on the platform ("pan") of a balance or scale. *(R. Wickham)*

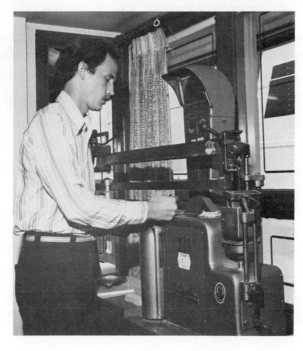

Figure 2.13
Inside the station: the two arms carrying the riders. *(R. Wickham)*

2.10 EXPERIMENT   THE MASS OF DISSOLVED SALT

In section 2.3, you learned that as salt dissolves in water, the combined volume of salt plus water decreases. This leads us to ask whether the mass also decreases when salt is dissolved in water.

Pour about 2 g of salt into the cap of a small plastic bottle, and put it carefully aside. Pour water into the plastic bottle until it is about two-thirds full. Find the total mass of the bottle, water, cap, and salt when all are on the balance together but the salt and water are not mixed.

Pour the salt into the bottle, and put the cap on. What is the mass of the capped bottle of salt and water? Shake the bottle occasionally to speed up the dissolving of the salt.

- Taking into consideration the precision of the balance, what do you conclude about the mass of salt and water as the salt dissolves?

Your answer to this question sums up the result of a single experiment. To have more confidence in your conclusion, you would have to repeat the experiment a number of times to check for possible errors. Many repetitions would use up much time and would not be very exciting. So, instead of asking you to repeat this experiment, we shall bring together the results of all the experiments done by the whole class. (We shall follow the same procedure with other experiments.) To see how class results compare and what their significance is, we shall display the mass differences in a histogram. Your teacher will show you how a histogram is made.

- Considering the precision of the balance, and all the results obtained by the class, what does your class conclude about the mass of salt and water as the salt dissolves?

- Can you suggest any reasons why all the members of the class do not get the same mass difference?

19† In Experiment 2.10, how could you recover the dissolved salt? How do you think its mass would compare with the mass of dry salt you started with?

20† If the change in mass of the salt and water solution was −0.0001 g in Experiment 2.10, would you have observed this change using your balance?

2.11 EXPERIMENT THE MASS OF ICE AND WATER

Here is another process involving a volume change. When ice melts, it contracts—its volume decreases. Does its mass also change?

Mass a small container with its cover; then put in an ice cube and mass again.

- What is the mass of the ice?

After all the ice has melted (if the container is not transparent, you can tell by shaking it), mass again.

- Do you notice any condensation of water on the outside of the container?

- If so, what should you do about it?

- What do you conclude about change in mass when ice melts?

2.12 EXPERIMENT THE MASS OF MIXED SOLUTIONS

In the two experiments you have just done, a solid was either dissolved or melted. Now let us ask what happens to the mass when a solid is formed by mixing two liquids.

Your teacher will provide you with samples of two solutions. Find the total mass of the bottles of solution and their caps. Now pour one solution into the same bottle with the other, and cap both bottles. Again find the total mass of both bottles.

- Did the mass change as a result of the mixing?

2.13 EXPERIMENT THE MASS OF COPPER AND SULFUR

The changes you have examined so far were quite mild. A more drastic change in matter takes place when sulfur and copper are heated together. Does the total mass change when these substances are heated together?

Put about 2 g of granular copper and about 1 g of sulfur in a test tube. (**CAUTION:** Do *not* use copper powder or copper dust. Also, be sure to wear safety glasses.) Close the end with a piece of rubber sheet held in place by a rubber band. Record the total mass of the closed tube. Heat the mixture gently until it begins to glow; then remove the flame immediately. (Let the test tube cool before you touch it.)

- Has the total mass of copper and sulfur changed?

Describe the appearance of the material in the test tube.

- Do you think the substance in the bottom is sulfur, copper, or a new substance?

21† The following data were obtained in an experiment in which copper and sulfur were made to react.

	Mass (g)
Tube and cover	20.484
Tube, cover, copper, and sulfur before reaction	23.440
Tube, cover, and products after reaction	23.386

a)   What is the mass of the substances before the reaction?
b)   What is the apparent change in mass of the reacting substances?
c)   What is the apparent percentage change in mass of the reacting substances?

22   A test tube having 4.00 g of iron and 2.40 g of sulfur was heated in a manner similar to that of the copper-and-sulfur experiment. The total mass of the tube and contents measured on the balance before the heating was 36.50 g. After the heating, its mass was measured again. The mass of the tube and contents was 36.48 g.
a)   Are you inclined to think it reasonable that mass remained the same—was conserved—during this experiment?
b)   What additional steps would you take to strengthen your inclination?

2.14 EXPERIMENT   THE MASS OF A GAS

In this experiment, a solid and a liquid produce a gas. Is there a change in mass?

CAUTION: You have been provided with a small *thick-walled* bottle wrapped with tape. Be sure to use this bottle only, and to wear safety glasses. Fill the bottle one-third full of water, then find the mass of the bottle, its cap, and *one-eighth* of an Alka-Seltzer tablet. Place the piece of tablet in the bottle. Immediately screw the cap on very tightly and place it back on the balance.

- Does what happens inside the bottle affect the mass of the bottle and its contents?

Slowly loosen the cap.

- Can you hear gas escaping?

Again mass the cap, the bottle, and its contents.

- What do you conclude?

2.15 THE CONSERVATION OF MASS

What have the last five experiments shown? If you have worked carefully, you have found that all the changes in mass that you observed were within the experimental error of your equipment. Therefore, your results agree with the conclusion that there was no change in mass that you could measure. From these experiments alone, you cannot predict with certainty that there will be no change in mass under other circumstances. For example, if we use larger amounts of matter in our experiments and use a balance of higher accuracy, we might measure a change greater than the range of experimental error. Then we would conclude that mass really does not remain the same. Furthermore, although we checked five rather different kinds of change, there is an endless variety of other reactions we could have tried, some even more violent than the reaction of copper and sulfur.

What would happen, for example, if we set off a small explosion inside a heavy steel case, making sure no mass escapes? The experiments you have done give no direct answer to this question. But we can make the guess that the results of these five experiments can be generalized in the following way: In all changes, mass is exactly conserved, provided nothing is added (like the water that condensed on the outside of the closed container in the experiment with ice and water) or allowed to escape (like the gas in the last experiment). This generalization is known as the law of conservation of mass. It has been checked to one part in a billion* for a large variety of changes. That is, experiments have been done in which a change in mass of one billionth of the total mass would have been observed if it had occurred.

Still, all this vast amount of evidence in favor of the law of conservation of mass does not prove that it will hold forever under all conditions. Surely, if someone claimed that he or she had done an experiment in which as much as one-millionth of the mass disappeared or was created, we should treat the results with great suspicion. First of all, we should make many checks to determine whether there had been a leak of some sort in the apparatus from which, say, gas could escape. The chances are that we should find such a leak. On the other hand, if an experiment were done in which a change in mass of one part in 100 billion was reported, we might have to conclude after a thorough examination of the experiment that the law of conservation of mass has its limitations, that it holds to one part in a billion but not to one part in 100 billion (10^{11}).

We have seen in this chapter that volume is very often a convenient way of measuring the quantity of matter. But we have also found out that, when matter changes form (when ice melts, salt dissolves, and so on), there is often an easily measurable change in volume but no observable change in mass: mass is conserved. It is the conservation of mass that makes mass such a useful measure of matter.

---

23 You wish to find your dog's mass, but the dog does not want to stand on the platform of the bathroom scale. You take the dog in your arms and stand on the scale; the mass indicated is 63 kg. Then you stand alone on the scale; the mass indicated is 55 kg.
   a) What is the mass of your dog?
   b) Give your reasoning.

24 a) Express the following numbers in powers of 10.
       100   10,000   100,000,000
   b) Write the following numbers without using exponents.
       10^5 10^6 10^9

---

*A billion is 1,000,000,000. Such a number is clumsy to write. Most of the zeros can be dispensed with by writing the number as 10^9 and reading it "ten to the ninth." The 9 is called an "exponent" and tells how many times we multiply 1 by 10 to get the number. For example, $1 \times 10 \times 10 = 10^2$, $1 \times 10 \times 10 \times 10 = 10^3$, and so on. We shall use this way of expressing numbers, called "powers-of-10 notation," whenever it is convenient. See the Appendix on pages 239–244 for further information.

c) Express the following numbers in powers of 10.
    1,000   5,280   93,000   690,000
d) Write the following numbers without using exponents.
    5.0×10^3 10^7 1.07×10^2 4.95×10^4

2.16 LAWS OF NATURE

The law of conservation of mass is the first of several laws of nature that we shall study in this course. It is worthwhile to pause at this point and compare the laws of nature with the laws of our society. Laws of society are legislated; that is, they are agreed upon and then enforced. If evidence is presented that you have broken such a law, you are punished. The laws of society can also be changed or repealed.

Laws of nature are quite different. These are guessed generalizations based on experiments, sometimes crude experiments. If you do an experiment that appears to violate a law of nature, you are not punished. On the contrary, if you present convincing evidence that the law is not quite true, the law is changed to take into account the new experience. Only rarely does this amount to a complete repeal of the law; in most cases the change is a recognition of the limitation of the law.

25 There is an old saying: "What goes up, must come down." Does this express a law of nature? Why, or why not?

For Home, Desk, and Lab

26 How would the volume of a piece of glass as measured by displacement of water compare with its volume as measured by displacement of burner fuel?

27 In determining the volume of a rectangular box, five cubes were found to fit exactly along one edge, and four cubes to fit exactly along another edge. However, after six horizontal layers had been stacked in the box, a space at the top was left unfilled.

Figure E
For problem 28

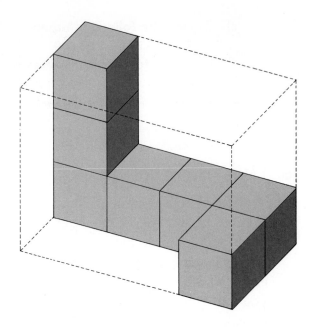

a) If the height of the space was half the length of an edge of a unit cube, what was the volume of the box?

b) If the height of the space was 0.23 of the length of an edge of a unit cube, what was the volume of the box?

28 What is the total number of cubes that will fit in the space enclosed by the dashed lines in Figure E? Is there more than one way to find an answer?

29 In an experiment in which the volume of dry sand is measured by the displacement of water, the sand was slightly wet to begin with. What effect would this have on the volume of air space that was calculated? On the percentage of the volume that was air space?

30 a) How would you measure the volume of a sponge?
    b) What have you actually measured by your method?
    c) Does this differ from your measurement of the volume of sand?

31 a) Completely fill two small bottles with water. Pour the water into a single larger vessel. Now refill the bottles with the same water. Are they both filled completely?
    b) Now do the same thing again, but fill one bottle with water and the other with burner fuel. Compare the total volume of burner fuel and water before and after they were mixed together and poured back into the bottles. Is volume a good measure for the quantity of matter in this case?

32 Fuel oil usually is sold by the gallon, gas for cooking by the cubic

foot, and coal by the ton. What are the advantages of selling the first two by volume and the last by mass?

33 In the following list of ingredients for a recipe, which are measured by volume, which by mass, and which by other means?

1½ pounds ground chuck   pinch of pepper
1 medium-size onion   3 drops Worcestershire sauce
½ cup chopped green pepper   oregano to taste
4 slices day-old bread   3 tablespoons oil
1 teaspoon salt   1 1-pound can tomato sauce

34 a) What is the volume of an aluminum cube whose edges are 10 cm long?
b) What is the mass of the aluminum cube? (One cubic centimeter of aluminum has a mass of 2.7 g.)

35 One cubic centimeter of gold has a mass of 19 g.
a) What is the mass of a gold bar 1.0 cm × 2.0 cm × 25 cm?
b) How many of these bars could you carry?

36 Suppose that you took a balance home. When you were ready to use it, you found that you had forgotten a set of gram masses.
a) How could you make a set of uniform masses from materials likely to be found in your home?
b) How could you relate your unit of mass to a gram?

37 Figure 11.11 (p. 244) shows a sensitive equal-arm balance. Suggest reasons why it is enclosed in a case and why it is used with the sliding front cover closed.

38 You wanted to find the mass of water in a plastic bottle, and you took the following measurements using your equal-arm balance.

Mass of bottle and water   21.48 g
Mass of empty bottle   9.56 g
Mass of water   11.92 g

After you completed your measurements and calculations, you saw that you forgot to set the left-hand rider correctly; the beam was not level when the right-hand rider was on the zero mark and nothing was on the pans of the balance. Must you repeat the measurements to obtain the mass of the water?

39 a) You can compare your standard masses on the equal-arm balance after you have carefully adjusted it. How closely is the 50-g mass equal to the sum of the 20-, 10-, 10-, 5-, 2-, 2-, and 1-g masses? How closely is the 5-g mass equal to the sum of the two 2-g masses and the 1-g mass? You can make other comparisons as well.

b)   When you are finding the difference in mass between an empty container and the container filled with liquid, why should you try to use as nearly as possible the same particular masses from your set for both measurements?

40   Suppose you lost the rider for your scale. Try to think of another method, not using a rider, by which you could measure hundredths of a gram.

41   Suppose you balance a piece of modeling clay on the balance. Then you reshape it. Will it still balance? If you shape it into a hollow sphere, will it still balance?

42   Suggest a reason for putting the lid on the small container that you used in studying the mass of ice and water.

43   In Experiment 2.11, would the mass of the container and its contents stay the same if you started with water and froze it? Try it.

44   Estimate in grams the mass of a wristwatch. Now find the mass of a nickel (5¢) on your balance. Estimate the mass of the watch again. Did you change your estimate? Does knowing the mass of a nickel help you to better estimate your own mass? Why?

45   Two astronauts on the moon use an equal-arm balance to find the mass of a specimen of moon rock; the specimen has a mass of 35.83 g. When the astronauts return to earth and mass the specimen once again, will they find that the mass of the rock on earth is more than, equal to, or less than the 35.83 g they measured on the moon?

 Themes for Short Essays

1   Suppose you are employed as a technical writer by a company that manufactures graduated cylinders. Printed instructions are to be included in packages sent out by the company. Write instructions telling customers how to use the cylinders correctly to measure the volumes of liquids.

2   A friend wants to use your equal-arm balance during the summer. Write a complete set of instructions for her so that she will be able to do so successfully without anybody being present to help her.

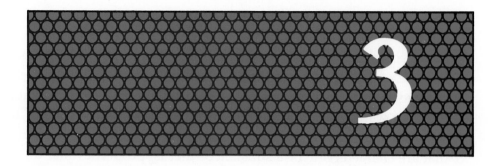

Characteristic Properties

3.1 PROPERTIES OF SUBSTANCES AND PROPERTIES OF OBJECTS

How do we know when two substances are different? It is easy enough to distinguish between wood, iron, and rock, or between water and milk; but there are other cases in which it is not so easy. Suppose that you are given two pieces of metal. Both look equally shiny and feel equally hard in your hand. Are they the same metal? Or think of two glasses containing liquids. Both liquids are transparent and have no smell. Are they the same or different?

To answer such questions, we shall have to do things to substances that will reveal differences which are not directly apparent. Merely massing the two pieces of metal will not do. Two objects can be made of different materials and yet have the same mass; think of a 100-g steel cylinder and a 100-g brass cylinder of the kind used as masses on a balance. On the other hand, two objects can have different masses and be made of the same materials: for example, two hammers, both made of steel but one much larger and with a greater mass than the other. Mass is a property of an object; it is not a property of the substance of which the object is made.

To find out if two pieces of metal that look alike are made of the same substance, you may try to bend them. Again, one can be thick and hard to bend, and the other can be thin and easy to bend; yet they can both be made of the same substance. On the other hand, you may find that two pieces of metal of different thicknesses but made of different substances bend with equal ease. Thus, ease of bending is also a property of the object and not of the substance.

If we want to find out whether two objects are made of the same substance or of different ones, we have to look for properties that are characteristic of a substance—that is, properties that do not depend on the amount of the substance or on the shape of the sample. In this chapter we shall concentrate on such properties—those that show differences between substances. These we call "characteristic properties."

---

1 **State which words in the following descriptions refer to properties of the substances and which refer to properties of the objects.**
   a) **A sharp, heavy, shiny, stainless-steel knife**
   b) **A small chunk of black tar**
   c) **A beautifully carved wooden chair**

3.2 EXPERIMENT   FREEZING AND MELTING

If you live in a part of the country where it snows in the winter, you know that a big pile of snow takes longer to melt than a small one. Does this mean that the big pile melts at a higher temperature? Let us see whether the temperature at which a sample of a substance melts or freezes is really a characteristic property of the substance. To do so, we shall measure the freezing temperatures of some substances by using samples of different mass. For convenience, we shall use substances that freeze above room temperature.

Fill a test tube one-third to one-half full with moth flakes or with moth nuggets and immerse it in a water bath. Heat the water until the solid in the test tube is completely melted. (Remember to wear safety glasses!) Insert a thermometer into the liquid. Make sure that the solid in the test tube is completely melted before removing the burner. For comparison, it may be interesting also to measure the temperature of the water with a second thermometer. (See Figure 3.1.) While the liquid cools, measure and record both temperatures every half-minute. (Stirring the water will ensure that the temperature will be the same throughout the water.)

In addition, record the temperature of the molten substance just as it begins to solidify. Continue to take readings every half-

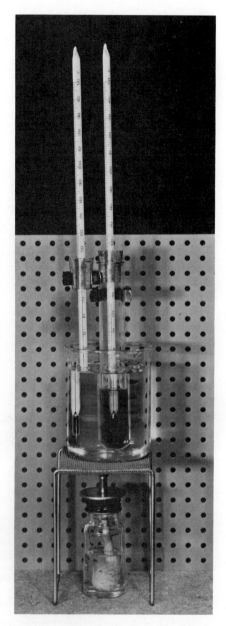

Figure 3.1
Apparatus used to obtain data for the cooling curve of a liquid as it cools and freezes. The thermometer in the test tube measures the temperature of the liquid; the one in the beaker measures that of the water bath. The thermometers are calibrated in degrees Celsius (°C).

minute until the temperature of the substance drops to about 45°C.

● In your table of temperatures and times, do you note any difference in the way the substance and the water cooled?

A better way to display your results is to plot the temperatures as a function of time on graph paper. Draw the graph of the temperatures of the substance and the water using the same axes. Compare your graphs with those of your classmates.

- Do all the graphs have a flat section?

- Does the temperature of the flat section depend on the mass of the cooling materials?

- Do you think that all the samples used in the class were of the same material?

———————

You have now determined the freezing point of a substance by noting the plateau (flat section) in the cooling curve. For some substances the plateau is more easily recognizable than it is for others. Some cooling curves, however, may not have a flat section at

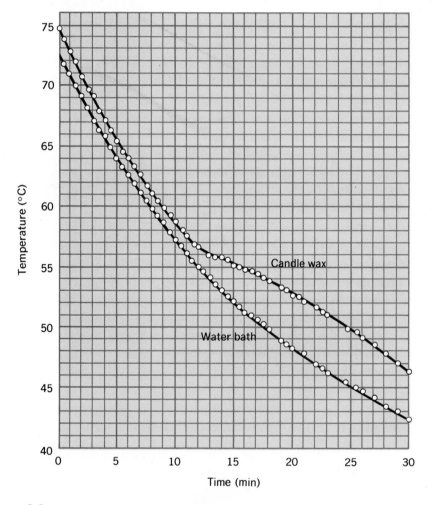

Figure 3.2
The cooling curves of candle wax and of the water bath surrounding the test tube holding the wax. The absence of a flat section in the curve for the wax means that candle wax has no freezing point.

all. For example, look at the cooling curve of candle wax shown in Figure 3.2. The data for this curve were obtained in the same way as in your experiment. The fact that no part of the curve is flat means that candle wax has no freezing point; that is, there is no temperature at which it changes from liquid to hard solid without continuing to cool down during the process. Similarly, as you warm a piece of candle wax in your hand, it becomes softer and softer, but there is no temperature at which it changes from hard solid to liquid without continuing to warm up.

It is harder to measure the melting point of a substance than to measure the freezing point; since we cannot stir a solid, it is necessary to heat it very slowly and evenly. If, however, we do very careful experiments to measure the melting point of a solid by heating it until it melts, we find that we get a curve with the flat portion at exactly the freezing temperature. A solid melts at the same temperature at which its liquid freezes.

2† **The graph in Figure A represents data from an experiment on the cooling of paradichlorobenzene. During which time intervals is there (a) only liquid, (b) only solid, and (c) both liquid and solid?**

Figure A
For problem 2

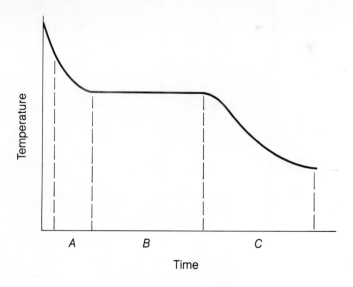

3 **Water freezes at 0°C. Sketch a graph of temperature versus time for a container of water at 20°C, after it is placed in a freezer at −10°C. Show the temperatures +20°C, 0°C, and −10°C on the vertical axis. Continue the graph until practically no further change will take place in the temperature of the ice.**

3.3 EXPERIMENT MICRO-MELTING POINT

In the preceding experiment, the quantities of moth flakes used by different students probably varied between 5 g and 10 g. This is a rather small range of mass. To give you confidence that the melting point is really a characteristic property, it is worthwhile to repeat the experiment with a *much* smaller sample—only a few tiny crystals.

To do this, you need a very small tube closed at one end to hold the crystals. Prepare this tube in the following way: Heat the center of a capillary tube in the alcohol flame. When the center melts, pull the two pieces apart, break off the glass thread, and seal the end of each piece in the flame. Crush between your fingers a small crystal of the material you used in the preceding experiment. Scoop up two or three bits of the smaller pieces in the open end of

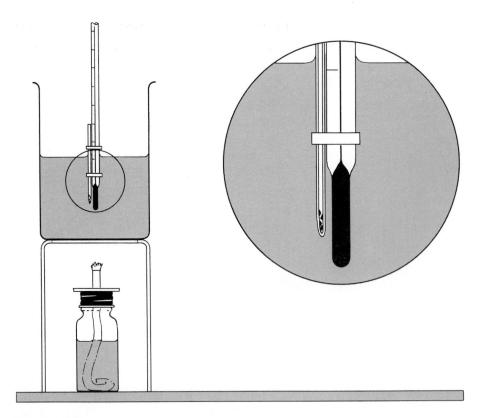

Figure 3.3
The melting point of a few tiny crystals of a substance can be measured by supporting a small capillary tube containing the crystals next to the bulb of a thermometer in a water bath.

one of the capillaries. By gently tapping the sealed end on the desk, you can make the tiny crystals fall to the bottom. Fasten the tube to the side of a thermometer with two rubber bands in such a way that the crystals are next to the thermometer bulb, as shown in Figure 3.3.

Support the thermometer in a beaker that is half-filled with water. Very slowly heat the water, while constantly observing the crystals.

- Should you stir the water during the heating? Why?

Be sure to read the thermometer the *instant* the crystals melt.

- At what temperature do the crystals melt?

You may need to use the other half of the capillary tube to make a second and more careful determination.

- How does the melting point compare with the freezing point you found when you cooled a large mass of the same substance?

- Roughly how many times larger was the large mass than one of the small crystals you melted?

- Does the melting point of a substance depend on the mass of the sample you use when you measure the melting point? Is it a characteristic property?

3.4   EXPERIMENT   BOILING POINT

Everybody knows that it takes longer to get a full pan of water to boil than a half-filled one. Does this mean that the full pan gets hotter? To see what happens, heat either 10 cm^3 or 20 cm^3 of a liquid in a test tube in the apparatus shown in Figure 3.4. To prevent uneven boiling, add a few small chips of porcelain to the liquid. The glass and the rubber tubes will prevent vapors from spreading into the room. The vapors will condense in the cooled test tube.

Some of the liquids you will be using may be flammable. To guarantee gentle heating, be sure to use the burner stand as shown

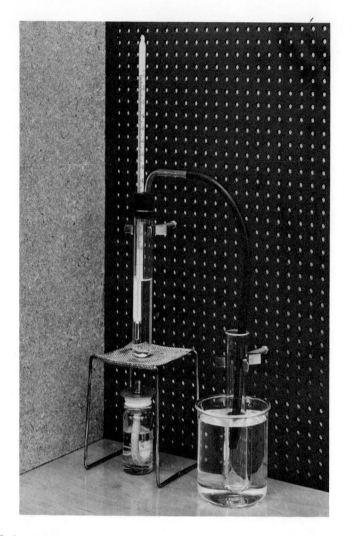

Figure 3.4
A thermometer supported by the cork in a test tube measures the temperature of the liquid as it is heated to its boiling point. To prevent uneven boiling, a few small chips of porcelain are placed in the liquid. The water in the beaker should be cold.

in Figure 3.4. Before you light the burner, remember to put on safety glasses!

Read the temperature of the liquid every half-minute until the liquid has been boiling for about five minutes. Then plot a graph of the temperature of the liquid as a function of time.

Compare your results with those of other students in your class.

- Do all the graphs look alike at the beginning?

- Do all the graphs have a flat section?

- Was the temperature the same in all test tubes once the liquid started boiling?

- What does a difference in boiling point reveal?

- Does the boiling point of a liquid depend on the amount of liquid? Is boiling point a characteristic property?

3.5 DENSITY

Suppose we cut a piece of aluminum rod into sections of equal volume—say, 1 cm³. We find that they all have the same mass when massed on a balance, no matter from what part of the rod they come. What if we take many 1-cm³ samples from a bottle of water? We find that each cubic centimeter of water has the same mass. However, the mass of 1 cm³ of water is different from the mass of 1 cm³ of aluminum rod. That is to say, the mass of a unit volume of material is the same for all samples of the same substance, but usually differs for different substances. The mass of a unit volume is, therefore, a characteristic property of a material. It can be used to distinguish one substance from another.

Rarely do we measure directly the mass of a unit volume of a sample of a substance. Usually we find that the volume of the sample is either larger or smaller than one unit volume. However, we can find the mass of a unit volume indirectly. We do this by measuring both the sample's mass and its volume. We then calculate the mass of one unit volume by dividing its mass by its volume. For example, consider a 30-g sample whose volume is 10 cm³. The mass of 1 cm³ of the material will be 30 g/10 = 3.0 g. Since each unit volume of a sample of a substance has the same mass, this indirect procedure will always give the same value for the mass of a unit volume as we would get by massing a sample whose volume is, in fact, one unit volume.

Because we generally find the mass of a unit volume by dividing mass by volume, we refer to it as mass *per* unit volume. (The word "per" means a division by the quantity that follows it. For example, the speed of a car is stated in miles *per* hour—that is, distance divided by time.) The mass per unit volume of a substance is called the "density" of the substance. Its units are g/cm³ (grams per cubic centimeter). In the example mentioned (p. 53), the density of the substance is 30 g/10 cm³ = 3.0 g/cm³. The two statements "The mass of 1 cm³ of the substance is 3.0 g" and "The density of the substance is 3.0 g/cm³" contain the same information. The second statement, however, is more concise.

---

4   A parking lot is filled with automobiles.
   a) Does the number of wheels in the lot depend upon the number of automobiles?
   b) Does the number of wheels per automobile depend upon the number of automobiles?
   c) Is the number of wheels per automobile a characteristic property of automobiles that distinguishes them from other vehicles?

5   a) Draw a graph of the number of wheels in a parking lot as a function of the number of cars.
   b) Draw a graph of the number of wheels per car as a function of the number of cars in the lot.

3.6   DIVIDING AND MULTIPLYING MEASURED NUMBERS

When you find the density of a substance from the measured mass and volume of a sample, your calculation uses numbers of limited accuracy. For example, consider a pebble that has a mass of 12.36 g and a volume of 4.7 cm³. Here the mass is given to four digits and the volume to two. If you calculate the quotient 12.36 g/4.7 cm³ on a calculator, you get the number 2.62978723. (You can, of course, do the division by hand to that many digits, if you have the patience.) However, not even a calculator can produce numbers that are more accurate than the data used in the calculations.

For division and multiplication, it is good to remember a simple rule of thumb: The result should have as many digits as the measured number with the smallest number of digits. It is always advisable to calculate one additional digit, and then round off. In the example we just saw, the density is

$$\frac{12.36 \text{ g}}{4.7 \text{ cm}^3} = 2.6 \text{ g/cm}^3$$

The only significant digits are 2.6. The remaining digits in the display of the calculator are not significant and should be dropped.

If we calculate the volume of an object from its dimensions, the same rule applies. If the measured dimensions of a rectangular solid are 4.82 cm, 11.05 cm, and 1.28 cm, then the volume is correctly reported as

$$4.82 \text{ cm} \times 11.05 \text{ cm} \times 1.28 \text{ cm} = 68.2 \text{ cm}^3$$

(68.17 cm^3 is rounded off to 68.2 cm^3.) It should *not* be reported as 68.174080 cm^3.

How do we count the digits in a decimal measurement whose last digit is a zero, as in the measurement 4.20 cm? (Section 2.2 explained why the zero is written.) In these cases, the zero is counted as a significant digit. However, in such measured numbers as 0.86 cm and 0.045 g, the zeros are not counted. Their only purpose is to locate the decimal point. Both these numbers are given to two significant digits.

---

6 Do the following calculations to the proper number of digits.

a) $\dfrac{125}{23.7}$ c) $\dfrac{0.065}{32.5}$ e) 4.72 × 0.52

                                    f) 6.3 × 10.08

b) $\dfrac{20.5}{51.0}$ d) $\dfrac{1.23}{0.72}$ g) 1.55 × 2.61 × 5.3

                                    h) 3.01 × 5.00 × 25.62

7 Suppose the measurement of the first dimension of the rectangular solid discussed above were 4.81 cm or 4.83 cm instead of 4.82 cm. Write all the digits in the number that would represent the volume of the solid. Which of these digits are the same as those calculated in the example above?

3.7 EXPERIMENT   THE DENSITY OF SOLIDS

Pick up two cubes that look alike and that have the same volume. Can you decide by handling them whether they have the same or different masses?

Measure the masses of the cubes on your balance.

Which of the cubes has the greater density?

Now, just by handling them, compare the mass of each of the cubes with the mass of a third object which has a different volume.

- Can you decide in this way if the third object is made of a different substance?

Measure the dimensions of each of the three objects as accurately as you can. Calculate the volume and then the density of each.

- Are you now able to decide whether or not the third object is made of the same substance as either of the other two cubes?

If you have an irregularly shaped object whose volume is difficult to determine from a measurement of its dimensions, you can find its volume by the displacement of water, as described in Chapter 2. Find the density of an irregularly shaped stone. Compare the density of your stone with the results of other students who used pieces from the same rock.

- What possible reasons could you give for the different measured values of density?

8† What measurements and what calculations would you make to find the density of the wood in a rectangular block?

9 A student announced that she had made a sample of a new material that had a density of 0.85 g/cm³. How large a sample had she made?

10† A block of magnesium whose volume is 10.0 cm³ has a mass of 17.0 g. What is the density of magnesium?

11 Two cubes of the same size are made of iron and aluminum. How many times as heavy as the aluminum cube is the iron cube? (See Table 3.1, page 63.)

12† a) A 10.0-cm³ block of silver has a mass of 105 g. What is the density of silver?
b) A 5.0-cm³ block of rock salt has a mass of 10.7 g. What is the density of rock salt?
c) A sample of alcohol amounting to 0.50 cm³ has a mass of 0.41 g. What is its density?

3.8 EXPERIMENT   THE DENSITY OF LIQUIDS

Examine two samples of liquid. Smell them and shake them, but don't taste them. Can you tell whether they are the same or different? Perhaps by finding their densities you can answer the question. You can find the density of a liquid by massing it on a balance and measuring its volume with a graduated cylinder. The cylinder is too large to fit easily on the balance. You must mass the liquid in something smaller.

A small amount of liquid will stick to the inside of any container from which you pour it. Therefore, to be sure you mass the volume of the liquid you measure in the graduated cylinder, you must be careful of the order in which you make your measurements of mass and volume.

- Is it more accurate to mass the liquid in the small container before pouring it into the graduated cylinder or to determine its volume first?

- What are the densities of the two liquids?

- Are the two liquids the same or different?

---

13 You are given two clear, colorless liquids. You measure the densities of these liquids to see whether they are the same substance or different ones.
a) What would you conclude if you found the densities to be 0.93 g/cm³ and 0.79 g/cm³?
b) What would you conclude if you found the density of each liquid to be 0.81 g/cm³?

3.9 THE HYDROMETER

The density of a mixture of two liquids usually depends on the ratio in which they are mixed. The same is true for the density of a solution of a solid in a liquid. Thus, knowing the density of a liquid can provide useful information. For example, the density of the liquid in a car's radiator tells us whether there is enough antifreeze (in most cases, glycol) in the mixture. Similarly, the density of the liquid in a car's battery tells us whether the battery should be recharged. Service station attendants, however, must be able to find densities in

Figure 3.5

The float of a hydrometer used to check car batteries. The dark portion at the bottom contains lead shot imbedded in wax. The narrower the upper part is with respect to the lower part, the more sensitive is the hydrometer.

less time than it takes you in the laboratory. To do that they use an instrument called a "hydrometer."

You have probably noticed that though an ice cube floats in water, it is almost submerged. The same ice cube will float higher in antifreeze. In general, a solid sinks in a liquid until the mass of the liquid it displaces equals its own mass. The operation of a hydrometer is based on this law.

The main part of the hydrometer is the float (Figure 3.5). The upper part of the float is narrow; the lower part is wide and contains some lead or other

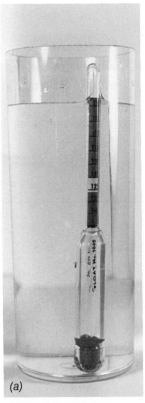

(a) (b) (c)

Figure 3.6

The float placed in liquids of different density.

Figure 3.7
The complete hydrometer in use. The purpose of the thermometer seen on the outside will be discussed in Chapter 12.

dense solid at the bottom. The mass at the bottom and the shape of the hydrometer are determined in such a way that the scale covers the desired range of densities. The float in Figure 3.5 was made to test car batteries. In Figure 3.6, it is placed in pure water and in two solutions of different densities. Note that the float is not designed to measure the density of pure water; in water it sinks to the bottom.

It is awkward and dangerous to pour the liquid out of a car's battery. Therefore, the float is placed in an outer cylinder equipped with a suction bulb. This way the liquid can be lifted directly out of the battery and then easily returned (Figure 3.7).

---

14 Which of the liquids shown in Figure 3.6 has the highest density?

3.10 EXPERIMENT   THE DENSITY OF A GAS

It is more difficult to measure the density of a gas than that of a liquid or a solid. Gases are hard to handle, and most of them cannot even be seen. In fact, early chemists neglected to take into account the mass of gases produced in experiments.

When we mix Alka-Seltzer tablets and water, a large volume of gas is produced. We can find the density of this gas by massing the tablets and the water before and after they are mixed and by collecting and measuring the volume of the gas. You will recall that, in Experiment 2.14, you measured the mass of some of this same gas, but you did not measure the volume.

Place two half-tablets of Alka-Seltzer and a test tube containing about 10 cm³ of water on the pan of your balance as shown in Figure 3.8, and find the total mass of these objects.

Arrange the apparatus as shown in Figure 3.9 so that you can collect the gas that will be evolved. Be sure the end of the rubber tube is at the top of the collecting bottle and that the whole length of the tube is clear and open. After putting on your safety glasses, drop the two half-tablets into the water, quickly insert the delivery

Figure 3.8
To support a test tube containing water on the balance, you can use a paper clip and a rubber band as shown. Be sure that the paper clip does not rub against the arm of the balance.

Figure 3.9
When the two half tablets are added to the test tube, the gas generated is collected by displacing water from the inverted bottle on the right.

tube and stopper into the test tube, and collect the gas produced. Practically all the gas will be produced in the first 10 minutes of the reaction. At the end of this time, remove the delivery tube from the bucket and then remove the stopper from the test tube.

- Why is it important to hold your hand across the mouth of the bottle while removing it from the bucket?

Turn the bottle upright, and find the volume of the water displaced by gas.

- How is this volume related to the volume of the gas?

- How can you find the mass of the gas?

- What is the density of the gas?

- What assumptions have you made in using this method?

15† A mixture of two white solids is placed in a test tube, and the mass of the tube and its contents is found to be 33.66 g. The tube is stoppered, and apparatus is arranged to collect any gas produced. When the tube is gently heated, a gas is given off, and its volume is found

to be 470 cm^3. After the reaction, the mass of the test tube and its contents is found to be 33.16 g.
a) What is the mass of the gas collected?
b) What is the density of the gas collected?

16 Experiment 3.10 is repeated with a sample of a different solid. Here are the data obtained:
Mass of solid, test tube, and water before action .... 35.40 g
Mass of test tube and contents after action .... 34.87 g
Volume of gas collected .... 480 cm^3
Could this gas be the same as that produced in Experiment 3.10?

17 The volume of gas generated by treating 1.0 g of magnesium carbonate with 8.8 g of sulfuric acid is 200 cm^3. The remaining acid and solid have a mass of 9.4 g. What is the density of the gas evolved?

18 If the volume of gas in the preceding problem is compressed to 50 cm^3, what will the density of the gas now be? To what volume must the gas be compressed before it will reach a density of 1.0 g/cm^3, a typical density of a liquid?

19 The gas whose density you measured in Experiment 3.10 dissolves slightly in water.
a) How does this affect the volume of the gas you collect?
b) How does this affect your determination of the density of the gas?

3.11 THE RANGE OF DENSITY

Table 3.1 lists the densities of various substances. Note that most solids and liquids have a density that is between 0.5 g/cm^3 and about 20 g/cm^3. The densities of gases are only about 1/1,000 of the densities of solids and liquids.

Is the density of a substance always the same? Most substances expand when heated, but their mass remains the same. Therefore, the density depends on the temperature, becoming less as the material expands and increases in volume. But, as we shall see in Chapter 12, the expansion is very small for solids and liquids and has little effect on the density. The situation is quite different for gases, which show a large thermal expansion. Moreover, we find it difficult to compress solids and liquids, but we can easily com-

Table 3.1 Densities of Some Solids, Liquids, and Gases (in grams per cubic centimeter)

Osmium	22.5	Oak	0.6-0.9	
Platinum	21.4	Lithium	0.53	
Gold	19.3	Liquid helium		
Mercury	13.6	(at $-269°C$)	0.15	
Lead	11.3	Liquid hydrogen		
Copper	8.9	(at $-252°C$)	0.07	
Iron	7.8	Carbon dioxide	1.8×10^{-3}*	At
Iodine	4.9	Oxygen	1.3×10^{-3}	atmospheric
Aluminum	2.7	Air	1.2×10^{-3}	pressure
Carbon		Nitrogen	1.2×10^{-3}	and
tetrachloride	1.60	Helium	1.7×10^{-4}	room
Water	1.00	Hydrogen	8.4×10^{-5}	temperature
Ice	0.92	Air at 20 km		
Methyl alcohol	0.79	altitude	9×10^{-5}	

* Small numbers less than 1 can, like large numbers, be expressed in powers of 10. For example, we write 0.1 as 10^{-1}, 0.01 as 10^{-2}, 0.001 as 10^{-3}, and so on, using negative numbers as exponents.

If we have decimals like 0.002, we can write this first as 2×0.001 and then, in powers-of-10 notation, as 2×10^{-3}. Another example: $0.00009 = 9 \times 0.00001 = 9 \times 10^{-5}$. The negative exponent of the 10 tells how many places the decimal point must be moved to the left to give the correct value in regular notation. For further information, see the Appendix (pages 287–292).

press gases, as you know from pumping up a bicycle tire. Therefore, when measuring the density of a gas, we have to state the temperature and the pressure at which it was measured.

---

20 Write the following numbers in powers-of-10 notation.
   a) 0.001   0.1   0.0000001
   b) 1/100   1/10,000

21 Write each of the following numbers as a number between 1 and 10 times the appropriate power of 10.
   a) 0.006   0.000032   0.00000104
   b) 6,000,000   63,700

22 Change the following numbers to ordinary notation.
   a) 10^{-2} 10^{-5} 3.7×10^{-4}
   b) 1.05×10^{-5} 3.71×10^{3}

23† A small beaker contains 50 cm³ of liquid.
   a) If the liquid were methyl alcohol, what would be its mass?
   b) If the liquid were water, what would be its mass?

24† **The densities in grams per cubic centimeter of various substances are listed below. Indicate which of the substances might be gas, liquid, or solid. (Refer to Table 3.1.)**
  (a) 0.0015   (b) 10.0   (c) 0.7   (d) 1.1   (e) 10^{-4}

25 **Estimate the mass of air in an otherwise empty room that is the size of your classroom.**

3.12   IDENTIFYING SUBSTANCES

We have looked for properties that can help us to distinguish between substances that appear to be the same. So far we have found three properties that do not depend on how much of a substance we have or on its shape. These properties are melting point, boiling point, and density.

Suppose we measured the melting points of two samples of matter and found them to be the same. If we then measured their boiling points and found that these were also the same, we might suspect that we had two samples of the same substance. We would not expect them to differ in their density or in any other properties. But, as Table 3.2 shows, we cannot depend on two properties alone to distinguish between substances. This is particularly true if the measurements are not highly accurate.

In Group 1 of the table, we have substances with the same boiling points and nearly the same melting points. It would be hard to measure these two properties carefully enough to see that they are different substances, but a measurement of their densities would prove without question that they are different.

The substances in Group 2 have the same density and nearly the same boiling point, but can be told apart by their different melting points.

If you compared only their densities, you might conclude that the three substances in Group 3 are the same. If you also measured their melting points, you would probably decide that the second and third substances in this group are the same. If you compared their densities and boiling points but not their melting points, which would you conclude are the same? In fact, all three substances in Group 3 are different. That is why they were given different names when first discovered.

20°C

Table 3.2   Some Substances with Similar Properties

	Density (g/cm³)	Melting point (°C)	Boiling point (°C)
Group 1			
Methyl acetate	0.93	−98	57
Acetone	0.79	−95	57
Group 2			
Isopropanol	0.79	−89	82
t-Butanol	0.79	26	83
Group 3			
Cycloheptane	0.81	−12	118
n-Butanol	0.81	−90	118
s-Butanol	0.81	−89	100

The names of the substances in this table are not important to us now, and you do not need to remember them. They are good examples of substances that we cannot tell apart unless we measure all three properties: density, melting point, and boiling point.

There are not very many examples of substances that are nearly the same in two of these three properties and yet differ in the third. We would have to search even harder to find two samples of matter that have the same density, melting point, and boiling point but that differ in some other property and are, in fact, samples of different substances. If we can determine density, melting point, and boiling point, we can distinguish between almost all substances.

In many cases, the melting point and the boiling point of a sample of matter can be measured easily in the laboratory. However, some substances have boiling points so high that it is difficult to get them hot enough to boil. For example, table salt boils at 1413°C. Others have boiling points so low that it is difficult even to get them cold enough to become liquid. The same experimental difficulties come up when we try to determine the melting points of some substances. Grain alcohol melts at −117°C.

Suppose we have a sample of a newly made substance. We wish to find out whether it is truly a new substance, different from all others, or a substance already known but made in a new way. If its boiling and melting points are too high or too low to measure easily, we must look for other characteristic properties that might help to distinguish it from similar substances.

26 Which of the substances listed in Table 3.2 are solids, which are liquids, and which are gases at (a) room temperature (20°C), (b) 50°C, (c) 100°C?

For Home, Desk, and Lab

27 Figure B shows a diagram of a double boiler. Why is the double boiler used to cook food that is easily scorched?

Figure B
For problem 27

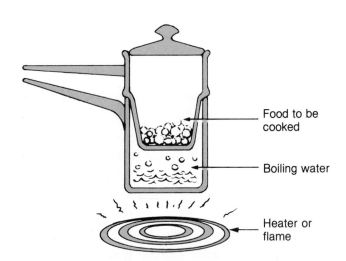

Food to be cooked

Boiling water

Heater or flame

28 Object A has a mass of 500 g and a density of 5.0 g/cm³; object B has a mass of 650 g and a density of 6.5 g/cm³.
    a) Which object would displace the most liquid?
    b) Could object A and object B be made of the same substance?

29 A student measures the volume of a small aluminum ball by water displacement and then finds its mass on a balance. He finds that the sphere displaces 4.5 cm³ of water. He determines that the mass of the sphere is 6.5 g.
    a) What value does the student obtain for the density of aluminum?

b) How might you account for the difference between this value for the density of aluminum and the one given in Table 3.1?

30 A student has several different-size specimens of substances C and D. She measures the masses and volumes of these specimens and plots the graphs shown in Figure C. Which substance has the greater density? How do you know?

Figure C
For problem 30

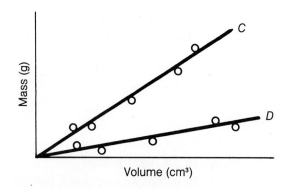

31 How would you determine the density of ice? Could you get the volume by melting the ice and measuring the volume of the resulting water?

32 How would you distinguish between unlabeled pint cartons of milk and of cream without breaking the seals?

33 **a)** Suppose you made your own hydrometer. Its mass is 11.5 g. What volume will the hydrometer displace in a liquid with a density of 1.20 g/cm^3?
    b) Suppose the lower part of your hydrometer has a volume of 7.0 cm^3, and the upper part is 5.0 cm long and has a cross-sectional area of 0.62 cm^2. What length of the upper part of the hydrometer will be submerged?

34 In Table 3.1, why are the pressure and temperature stated for the densities of gases and not stated for the densities of solids and liquids?

35 The students in an *IPS* class in one of the coastal cities of the United States measured the boiling point of water and found that it was 100°C. On the same day the students in an *IPS* class in one of the mountain cities in the United States also measured the boiling point of water and found that it was 95°C. What can be inferred about the boiling point of water from these reports?

36 A cylinder is closed with a tight-fitting piston 30 cm from the end wall (Figure D); it contains a gas with a density of 1.2×10^{-3} g/cm³. The piston is pushed in until it is 10 cm from the end wall; no gas escapes. What is the density of the compressed gas? What is your reasoning?

Figure D
For problem 36

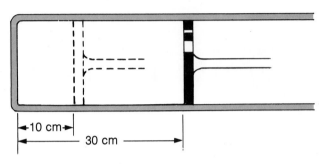

←10 cm→

←———— 30 cm ————→

37 Does the density of air change when it is heated:
a) in an open bottle?
b) in a tightly stoppered bottle?

Themes for Short Essays

1 Ice floats on water. Suppose it did not. What would happen to life in lakes and rivers? Write a short science-fiction story on this subject.

2 Write a short mystery story in which a crook tries to pass off a small statue of gold-plated lead as solid gold. Have the detective uncover the plot without damaging the statue.

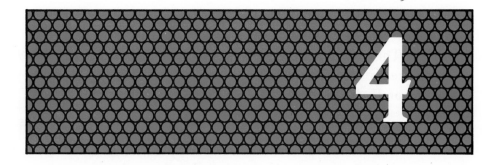

4

Solubility

4.1 EXPERIMENT DISSOLVING A SOLID IN WATER

You know from daily experience that sand and chalk do not dissolve in water, but that sugar and table salt do. Of course, these are only qualitative observations—that is, observations that do not involve measurement. Are you sure that not even a tiny amount of chalk dissolves in a gallon of water? Can you dissolve as much salt in a glass of water as you wish?

Many solutions are colorless—there is nothing to be seen once the solid is dissolved. To make things visible, we shall begin our quantitative study of solutions with a solution that has color.

Place 5.0 cm^3 of water in one test tube and 20.0 cm^3 of water in another. Add 0.30 g of orange solid to each tube, then stopper and shake thoroughly. **CAUTION:** Be careful not to get any of the solution on your hands. If some spills, wash thoroughly with water.

- Did all of the solid dissolve in both test tubes?

- Do you think that each cubic centimeter of solution contains the same mass of dissolved material?

- Both tubes contain the same mass of dissolved material, but is the shade of the color the same in both tubes?

- Will another 0.30 g of the orange solid dissolve in each of the test tubes? Try it, but be patient!

The solution may cool as the solid dissolves. If so, try to keep the temperature fairly constant by warming the test tube with your hand.

- Did 0.60 g of solid dissolve as well in 20.0 cm³ as in 5.0 cm³ of water?

- Is the color uniform in each solution?

- Is the shade of the color the same in both solutions?

Add another 0.30 g of the orange solid to each solution.

- How much do you have in each test tube?

- What do you observe?

- How much orange solid do you think there would have to be in the 20.0-cm³ test tube so that not all of it will dissolve? Test your prediction.

A solution in which no more solid can be dissolved is called a "saturated" solution.

4.2   CONCENTRATION

The uniformity of color in any one of the various solutions in the last experiment suggests that the solid dissolved uniformly. That is, a cubic centimeter of water in a given solution contained the same mass of orange material as any other cubic centimeter of water in that solution. For example, at the beginning of the experiment one test tube had 0.30 g/5.0 cm³ = 0.060 g/cm³ of material and the other test tube had 0.30 g/20.0 cm³ = 0.015 g/cm³.

The mass of solid dissolved per unit volume of liquid is called the "concentration" of the solution. This unit is the same as that of density, g/cm³. However, in the case of density, the mass and the volume refer to the same substance. In the case of concentration, the mass refers to the dissolved solid (called the "solute") and the volume refers to the liquid (called the "solvent").

To avoid confusion and for other reasons of convenience, concentrations are often given in g/100 cm³.

A concentration of 0.015 g/cm³ means that 0.015 g of solute is dissolved in 1 cm³ of water. A volume of 100 cm³ of water will, therefore, contain 100 × 0.015 g = 1.5 g of solute. Therefore, the concentration of the solution in $g/100 \text{ cm}^3$ is $1.5 \text{ g}/100 \text{ cm}^3$. In general, to find the concentration of a solution in $g/100 \text{ cm}^3$, we multiply the concentration in g/cm^3 by 100.

---

1   For Experiment 4.1, calculate the concentration of the solutions in g/cm^3 and in $g/100 \text{ cm}^3$ after the addition of each sample of solid.

2   What can you say about the largest concentration you were able to make in the experiment?

3   A mass of 25.0 g of sugar is dissolved in 150 cm^3 of water. What is the concentration in $g/100 \text{ cm}^3$?

4.3   EXPERIMENT   COMPARING THE CONCENTRATIONS OF SATURATED SOLUTIONS

From the results of dissolving the orange solid (Experiment 4.1), you know that you will reach a point where no more solute will dissolve in the solvent. The solution then has the largest possible concentration and is called a saturated solution, as said in section 4.1.

To find the concentration of a saturated solution, you could add a tiny amount of solid at a time and see whether it dissolves. A better method is to begin with a large mass of solid and shake it until you judge that no more will dissolve. Then you can pour off some of the clear liquid and find the concentration.

Try dissolving 5 g of two solids in separate test tubes, each containing 5 cm^3 of water. Stopper the test tubes, and shake them vigorously for several minutes until you have a saturated solution. If the tube cools during the process, keep it warm with your hand.

- Does one sample of solid appear to be more soluble in water than the other?

To find the concentrations of the two saturated solutions, you can evaporate the liquid from a known mass of each solution. Subtracting the mass of the remaining dry solid from the mass of the solution will give you the mass and, therefore, the volume of the water of your sample. This will give you the data you need to calculate the concentration of the saturated solution. You can do the experiment for one solution while some of your classmates work with the other solution.

Pour almost all the saturated solution into a previously massed evaporating dish, being careful not to pour out so much solution that undissolved solid is carried over from the test tube into the dish.

After finding the total mass of dish and solution, you can slowly evaporate the saturated solution to dryness over a flame, as shown in Figure 4.1 (below), and find the mass of the remaining solid. Be careful to heat the solution very slowly so that solid does not spatter out of the dish. Keep watching the dish, and move the flame away whenever spattering begins.

- What was the mass of the solid and the mass of the water in which it dissolved?

- What was the volume of the water?

- What was the concentration of each of the saturated solutions?

- How do your results compare with those of your classmates?

The concentration of a saturated solution is called the "solubility." In this experiment, you found the solubilities of two substances in the same solvent, namely water.

Solubility is independent of the mass of the sample from which it is found. It is a characteristic property of the combination of the solute and the solvent.

Figure 4.1

Evaporating a solution in an evaporating dish heated over an alcohol burner. If the liquid spatters, it should be heated more slowly by moving the burner to one side so that the flame heats only one edge of the dish.

4 Mario wishes to construct a table that lists the solubility in water of several substances. From various sources he finds the following data for solubilities at 0°C.

   a) Boric acid   0.20 g in 10 cm³ of water
   b) Bromine   25 g in 600 cm³ of water
   c) Washing soda   220 g in 1,000 cm³ of water
   d) Baking soda   24 g in 350 cm³ of water

   What is the solubility of each substance in grams per 100 cm³ of water?

5 From your answers to problem 4, find the largest mass of each substance that will dissolve in 60 cm³ of water.

6 Suppose that 200 cm³ of a saturated solution of potassium nitrate were left standing in an open beaker on your laboratory desk for three weeks. During this time most of the water evaporated. Would the mass of potassium nitrate dissolved in the solution change? Would the concentration of the potassium nitrate solution change during the three weeks?

4.4 EXPERIMENT   THE EFFECT OF TEMPERATURE ON SOLUBILITY

In the last experiment, you tried to keep the temperature of the solution constant (by warming the test tube with your hand if it cooled). How will the solubility of different substances be affected by the temperature of the liquid? Remember that solubility is the maximum mass of a solid that will dissolve in a given volume of liquid.

   To find out, add 10 g of two solids to test tubes, each containing 10 cm³ of water. Place both test tubes in a large beaker of water, and stir the solutions for several minutes until they are saturated. Now heat the beaker, stirring both solutions constantly, until the water in the beaker is near boiling.

   • What do you observe?

   • Do the solubilities of the substances appear to change equally or differently as the temperature of the water is increased?

- What do you predict will happen if you remove the burner and cool both test tubes together in a beaker of cold water? Try it.

———————————————

Figure 4.2 shows the result of an experiment with potassium sulfate. The solubilities at different temperatures were measured by the same method you used in Experiment 4.3. The solubility is expressed as the mass in grams of the substance that is dissolved in 100 cm³ of water to give a saturated solution or, to put it another way, the maximum mass of the substance that can be dissolved in 100 cm³ of water.

Suppose we dissolve 20 g of potassium sulfate in 100 cm³ of water at 80°C. If we now cool the solution to room temperature, 25°C, Figure 4.2 shows that the water can hold only 12 g of potassium sulfate in solution at this temperature. Therefore, during the cooling process, small crystals of solid potassium sulfate begin to appear in the solution at about 70°C. As cooling continues, more crystals are produced in the solution, and they sink to the bottom. A solid that crystallizes out of a saturated solution in this manner is

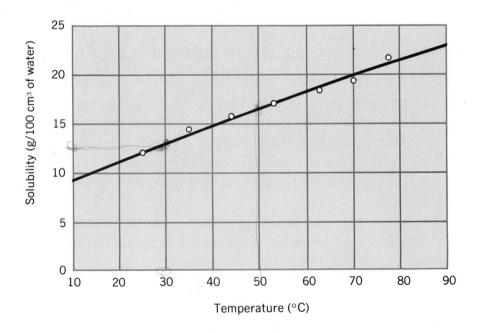

Figure 4.2
A graph of the solubility of potassium sulfate as a function of temperature. The graph shows the maximum concentration of potassium sulfate solution at different temperatures.

called a "precipitate." As you can see from Figure 4.2, the mass of potassium sulfate that will precipitate out of solution and collect at the bottom in this case will be 20 g − 12 g = 8 g.

Figure 4.3 shows the solubility as a function of temperature for several other common substances, all plotted together in the same graph. These curves clearly show that the way the solubility of a substance changes with temperature is a characteristic property that can help to distinguish between different substances. You can see from the graph, for example, that the solubilities of potassium nitrate and sodium chloride (ordinary table salt) are very nearly the same at room temperature (about 25°C) but are widely different at high and low temperatures.

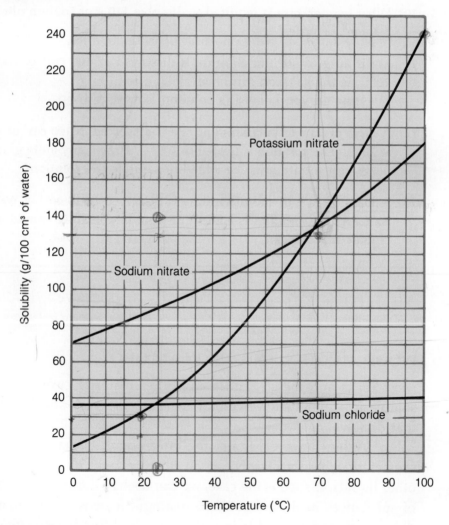

Figure 4.3
Solubility curves of different substances dissolved in water as a function of temperature.

7 If you plotted the data from Figure 4.2 on Figure 4.3, where would the graph be found?

8 Suppose you have a saturated solution of potassium nitrate at room temperature. From Figure 4.3, what do you predict will happen if you
a) heat the solution?
b) cool the solution?

9 What reason can you give for heating the solutions in Experiment 4.4 by immersing the test tubes in a beaker of hot water rather than heating the test tubes directly over a burner flame?

10† What temperature is required to dissolve 110 g of sodium nitrate in 100 cm³ of water?

11 a) If 20 g of sodium chloride is dissolved in 100 cm³ of water at 20°C, is the solution saturated?
b) How do you know if a solution is saturated?

12† A mass of 30 g of potassium nitrate is dissolved in 100 cm³ of water at 20°C. The solution is heated to 100°C. How many more grams of potassium nitrate must be added to saturate the solution?

13 A mass of 10 g of sodium nitrate is dissolved in 10 cm³ of water at 80°C. As the solution is cooled, at what temperature should a precipitate first appear?

4.5 WOOD ALCOHOL AND GRAIN ALCOHOL

Most rocks and metals, and many other materials, are so slightly soluble in water that we cannot measure the very small amounts that dissolve.

Water, however, is not the only liquid. Perhaps some substances that hardly dissolve at all in water will dissolve easily in other liquids. If such is the case, we can use the different solubilities of substances in these liquids to distinguish between them, as we did with materials soluble in water. We shall first investigate wood alcohol and grain alcohol, two common liquids. Then we shall see if there are other solvents that will further increase our stock of tools for investigating matter.

Wood alcohol, as its name implies, was first made from wood. In fact, some of the liquid that you collected in your distillation of wood was wood alcohol. The ancient Syrians heated wood in order to obtain the liquids and tars that resulted. The watery liquids (including the alcohol mixed with other liquids) were used as solvents and as fuel for lamps. The tars were used to fill the seams in boats, to preserve wood against rot, and as mortar for bricks.

The method used by the Syrians in making these substances was the same as the one you used when you distilled wood, although the apparatus they used was cruder. Lengths of wood were stacked closely in a dishlike depression in the top of a mound of earth. A drain ran from the middle of the depression to a collection pit. After the wood was covered with green branches and wet leaves, a fire was started inside the pile. As this fire smoldered, watery liquids and tars drained off from the pile and collected in the pit. Later it was discovered that the watery liquids could be separated, just as you separated them after you distilled wood. One of these liquids was wood alcohol.

Grain alcohol can be made by fermenting grains, such as corn, barley, and rye, and also by fermenting grapes and other fruits. Fermentation is the process that goes on naturally when fruit juices or damp grain are stored with little exposure to air. Gas bubbles out of the liquid, and what remains boils at a temperature lower than the boiling point of water. As had been discovered long before the beginning of recorded history, this liquid contained a new substance different from water. It was used as a beverage (with effects quite different from those of water) and as a medicine.

Some time before the twelfth century, the wine from fermented grapes was first distilled, and the condensed liquid was described as the "water that burns." It was named *alcohol vini* or "essence of wine," and later came to be called "grain alcohol."

If we measure the densities of the alcohols we get from different grains and fruits, we find no difference between them. These alcohols also have the same boiling point and melting (or freezing) point. In fact, they are all the same substance. Similarly, the alcohols (or essences) produced from different kinds of wood are all

Table 4.1   Some Characteristic Properties of the Most Common Alcohols

	Density (g/cm³)	Melting point (°C)	Boiling point (°C)
Wood alcohol (methanol)	0.79	−98	64.7
Grain alcohol (ethanol)	0.79	−117	78.5

the same: all have the same density, boiling point, and melting point. Since the distilled liquids obtained from wood and fermented grain are both called alcohol, you might think that they are the same substance. But from an examination of Table 4.1, we see that they are indeed different. Though their densities are nearly the same, their melting points and boiling points differ enough so that there can be no possibility that they are the same substance. Today, wood alcohol is called "methanol," and grain alcohol is called "ethanol."

Both alcohols can be used as fuels. The fuel in your laboratory burner should contain mostly ethanol. Ethanol is the important ingredient in alcoholic beverages; methanol, on the other hand, is very poisonous. Some methanol, or other poison, is usually added to burner fuel to make it undrinkable; ethanol treated this way is said to be "denatured." Both will dissolve many substances that are insoluble in water, and these alcohols have been used as solvents for centuries.

---

14   You distilled wood in Experiment 1.1. Where would you expect to find the methanol at the end of the stage of the experiment shown in Figure 1.2? In Figure 1.3?

4.6   EXPERIMENT   METHANOL AS A SOLVENT

Sugar and citric acid look the same. They are both white. Sugar has a density of 1.59 g/cm³, and citric acid has a density of 1.54 g/cm³. These densities differ slightly—by only about 3 percent. You would find it difficult indeed to determine the volume of an irregular piece of either material to within 3 percent. The values that you would get for the densities of these substances could be no more accurate than your values for the volumes; and if either of these was in error by 3 percent or more, you could not be sure from your density determination whether the two materials were the same substance or not. It is also difficult to distinguish between these substances by their solubilities in water, because both are about equally soluble in water.

Suggest a way to distinguish between these substances by their solubility in methanol, and have your teacher approve it before you start. **CAUTION:** Do not inhale methanol vapor.

- Do the solubilities of sugar and citric acid in methanol help in distinguishing between the two substances?

You can also test the solubilities of other substances, such as moth flakes, magnesium, and magnesium carbonate.

- Do moth flakes dissolve in water? In methanol?

- Do magnesium and magnesium carbonate dissolve in water? In methanol?

You can now see how much we have enlarged our collection of tools for distinguishing between substances. We do not always have to measure density, melting point, or boiling point. For example, suppose we have two test tubes of colorless liquids and we place a piece of copper in each. If the copper dissolves in one but not in the other, we know the two liquids are different. Similarly, if we have two samples of white crystals that dissolve equally well in one solvent, but do not dissolve equally well in another solvent, then they are different substances. You saw an example of this in the case of sugar and citric acid.

15† Two solids appear to be the same and are both insoluble in methanol. A student, whose results are reliable to 5 percent, reports the solubilities of the two solids in water, as in the following table. Are these solids the same substance? Explain your answer.

Solid	Solubility (g/100 cm³)	
	0°C	100°C
A	73	180
B	76	230

16 a) **Which of the following substances, X, Y, and Z, do you think are the same?**

b) **How might you test them further to make sure?**

Substance	Density (g/cm^3)	Melting point $(°C)$	Boiling point $(°C)$	Solubility in water at $20°C$ $(g/100 \ cm^3)$	Solubility in methanol at $20°C$
X	1.63	80	327	20	insoluble
Y	1.63	81	326	19	insoluble
Z	1.62	60	310	156	insoluble

4.7 SULFURIC ACID

Another solvent useful in distinguishing between different substances was first produced more than a thousand years ago by heating a soft rock called "green vitriol." The vapors produced by heating the rock were cooled and condensed to form an oily liquid, which was called "oil of vitriol." Its modern name is "sulfuric acid." The ancient method of producing this acid has been abandoned in favor of a far more effective process of manufacture that starts with sulfur. As a result, the acid is readily available in large quantities. It is of great importance in industry and is used in the manufacture of many other substances.

One of the useful properties of sulfuric acid is its ability to dissolve some substances that will not dissolve in water. In many cases, when a substance is dissolved in sulfuric acid, a gas is given off. We shall investigate two such gases in the next experiment.

4.8 EXPERIMENT TWO GASES

One of the substances that produce a gas when dissolved in sulfuric acid is magnesium. To collect the gas, you can use the same apparatus as in Experiment 3.10. (**CAUTION:** Sulfuric acid is highly corrosive, so try not to spill it or get any on your hands, clothing, or books. If you do, wash it off immediately with water and tell your teacher. Be sure to wear your safety glasses.) Use about half a test tube of acid and five 7-cm lengths of magnesium ribbon to produce several test tubes of gas.

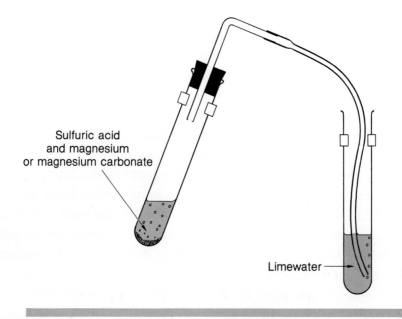

Figure 4.4
The limewater test. Gas from the test tube on the left is bubbled
through limewater in the one on the right.

- Should you discard the gas collected in the first test tube?
  Why?

Try lighting tubes of the gas, using first a burning splint and
then a glowing one. Try it holding some of the tubes upside down
and some right-side up.

- Does the gas burn?

- Is the gas more dense or less dense than air?

Try bubbling a little of the gas into limewater (Figure 4.4).
Repeat the experiment, using magnesium carbonate instead
of magnesium.

4.9 HYDROGEN

The gas you made by dissolving magnesium in sulfuric acid was
first produced many centuries ago by the action of sulfuric acid on
metals. It was called "inflammable air" because it burned. Later, it
was discovered that when inflammable air burns, it produces

another gas, which can easily be condensed to a liquid. This liquid was found to boil at 100°C, freeze at 0°C, have a density of 1.00 g/cm³, and dissolve the same substances that water does. In fact, all the properties of this liquid were the same as those of water, and so it was considered highly unlikely that it could be anything else. Because it produced water when it burned, the gas was given the name "hydrogen" about 200 years ago. "Hydro" is a prefix that means "water"; "gen" is a suffix that means "producing" or "generating."

However, other gases also give water when burned and, like hydrogen, are less dense than air. For many years, these gases were thought to be the same as hydrogen. Marsh gas, now called "methane," is an example that has been known for thousands of years. It is often produced by vegetable matter decaying at the bottoms of lakes or marshes, where it slowly bubbles up to the surface of the water. But this gas does not have nearly as low a density as hydrogen, and so it must be a different substance. It was not until the density of gases could be measured with reasonable accuracy that marsh gas was found to be a different substance from hydrogen.

---

17   **A student might try to find the density of hydrogen by the method you used for finding the density of a gas in Experiment 3.10, where you collected about 400 cm³ of gas.**
a)   What would be the mass of this volume of hydrogen?
b)   What difference in mass would there be between the total mass of test tube, acid, and magnesium at the start, and the total mass of test tube and contents at the end of the action?
c)   Could you accurately measure this difference in mass on your balance?

4.10   CARBON DIOXIDE

The gas that you produced by dissolving magnesium carbonate in sulfuric acid is called "carbon dioxide." It is a part of the air we exhale at every breath and is also produced by a variety of substances when they are placed in sulfuric acid. The density of carbon dioxide is 1.8×10^{-3} g/cm³, which is much greater than that of air. Since carbon dioxide does not burn, it makes a good fire extinguisher. It simply smothers the fire like a blanket.

Solid carbon dioxide, called "dry ice," evaporates directly

into carbon dioxide gas without first turning into a liquid. But, like melting ice, it stays cold until all the solid is gone. Ice melts at 0°C, but dry ice evaporates at a much lower temperature (at −78.5°C). It remains at this temperature as it evaporates, and for this reason it is often used to cool things down to very low temperatures.

4.11   THE SOLUBILITY OF GASES

If the gases we have investigated so far had been very soluble in water, we could not conveniently have collected them over water. They would simply have dissolved as fast as we produced them. In fact, these gases are so insoluble that it would be difficult to measure the amount of each that dissolves and then distinguish between them by their solubility.

Nevertheless, no gases are completely insoluble in water, and it is fortunate that gases do dissolve. Fish, for example, obtain the oxygen they need from oxygen dissolved in the water around them.

When carbon dioxide is dissolved in water, it changes the properties of water as a solvent. For example, calcium carbonate (the main ingredient of limestone and chalk) is much more soluble in water that contains carbon dioxide than in water that does not. Raindrops dissolve carbon dioxide as they pass through the atmosphere. When rain water enters the soil and hits a layer of limestone, it slowly dissolves the limestone, leaving an empty space. When the soil above this empty space can no longer support itself, it collapses (Figure 4.5).

18† In certain shallow parts of Long Island Sound, fish have been found dead of oxygen starvation on extremely hot days, though at other times fish live there very happily. What property of oxygen do these facts suggest?

19 Experiment 3.10 was performed twice, but with one tablet and 15 cm³ of water in each case. When the rubber tube was placed as shown in Figure 3.9, 435 cm³ of gas was collected. When the tube reached only slightly beyond the mouth of the bottle, only 370 cm³ of gas was collected. The change in mass of the reactants was the same in both cases.

  a) What volume of gas dissolved in the water?

Figure 4.5
A "sinkhole" in central Florida. Limestone below the top layer was dissolved in water containing much carbon dioxide. (*AP/Wide World Photos*)

b) Use Table 3.1 (page 63) to find what mass of gas dissolved in the water.

20 The solubility of chalk in water is 10^{-3} g/100 cm³. How much water would be necessary to dissolve a piece whose mass is 5 g?

4.12 EXPERIMENT   THE SOLUBILITY OF AMMONIA GAS

There are gases that are very soluble in water. A common example is ammonia, whose solution in water is used as a household cleaner. Figure 4.6 shows how ammonia gas can be produced by slowly heating a water solution of ammonia. The gas can then be collected in a dry test tube.

Collect a test tube of the gas. (Don't try to smell it directly—it is very irritating.) Then, very slowly, remove the tube and close it

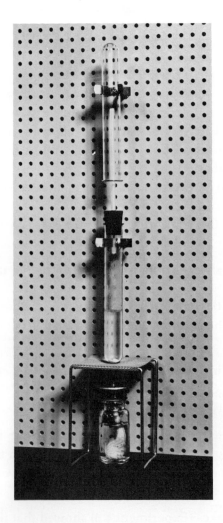

Figure 4.6
Collecting ammonia gas produced by
heating a water solution of the gas.

with a stopper. Place it, mouth downward, in a beaker of water, and
then remove the stopper.

- What do you observe?

- From the way you produced the gas, what can you conclude about the solubility of the gas as the temperature of
  the solution is raised?

- From the method of collecting the gas, what can you conclude about its density?

21† If the tube of ammonia gas had been inverted and placed in water
saturated with ammonia, would the liquid have risen in the test
tube as it did in this experiment?

22 Each of four test tubes contains 10 cm³ of water at 25°C. The following masses of an unknown solid are placed in the test tubes: 4 g in the first, 8 g in the second, 12 g in the third, and 16 g in the fourth. After the tubes are shaken, it is observed that all of the solid has dissolved in the first two tubes, but that there is undissolved solid in the remaining two tubes.
a) What is the concentration of the solid in each of the first two tubes?
b) What can you say about the concentration of the solid in the second two tubes?

23 a) Which of the substances shown in Figure 4.3 could be the unknown solid of problem 22?
b) If the unknown is indeed the substance you named in answer to part (a), what will happen if the solution in each test tube is cooled to 10°C?

24 The solubility of a substance in water was found to be 5 g/100 cm³ at 25°C, 10 g/100 cm³ at 50°C, and 15 g/100 cm³ at 75°C. What would you expect its solubility to be at 60°C? At 100°C? Explain.

25 In many localities, after a kettle has been used for some time for boiling water, a flaky solid appears on the inside-bottom and on the sides of the kettle that have been in contact with the water. How do you account for the presence of this "boiler scale"?

26 Your experiment with moth flakes (Experiment 4.6) showed that this substance was insoluble in water but that it dissolved readily in methanol.
a) Predict the effect of adding water to a methanol solution of moth flakes. Try it.
b) Sugar proved to be almost insoluble in methanol but dissolved readily in water. Predict the effect of adding methanol to a solution of sugar in water. Try this too.

27 There are two kinds of felt-tip (magic-marker) pens. Some are labeled "permanent" and some are labeled "water color."
a) What does the label tell you about the solubility in water of the dye in the two inks?
b) Do you think the liquid in both inks is water?

28 In dry cleaning, a garment is sprayed with liquids that dissolve various stains. Often a brightly colored cotton shirt carries a label: "Dry clean only—colors may bleed when washed."

a) What does this tell you about the solubility of the dye in hot water containing a detergent or soap?

b) Do you think the dye dissolves in cold tap water?

29 In Experiment 4.8, you found that magnesium metal would dissolve in sulfuric acid.

a) Does this observation enable you to predict with certainty that all metals will dissolve in sulfuric acid?

b) Try dissolving other metals, such as copper, zinc, lead, and aluminum, in sulfuric acid.

30 When magnesium carbonate is placed in sulfuric acid, a gas is produced whose properties you studied in Experiment 4.8. When you place washing soda in hydrochloric acid, you also get a gas. What would you do with this gas to determine whether it is the same gas that you got from dissolving magnesium carbonate in sulfuric acid?

31 Three samples of gas are tested for characteristic properties. Sample A does not turn limewater milky, is less dense than air, and burns. Sample B turns limewater milky, is more dense than air, and burns. Sample C turns limewater milky, is less dense than air, and burns. What can you conclude about these samples of gas?

32 A fizzing tablet is dissolved in 10 cm^3 of water, and the gas is collected as in Experiment 3.10. The volume of gas collected is 450 cm^3. When 50 cm^3 of water is used, the volume of gas collected is 405 cm^3. The tube was all the way up in the bottle in both cases.

a) Why do you think the volume is less?

b) Would this make a difference in the density calculation?

33 The following table shows the solubility of carbon dioxide at atmospheric pressure at various temperatures.

Solubility (g/100 cm^3)	Temperature (°C)
0.34	0
0.24	10
0.18	20
0.14	30
0.12	40
0.10	50
0.086	60

a) Draw a graph from these data.

b) Find, from your graph, how much carbon dioxide will dissolve in 100 cm^3 of water at 25°C.

c) Use Table 3.1, page 63, to find the volume of carbon dioxide that will dissolve in 100 cm^3 of water at room temperature (20°C).

d) How much carbon dioxide will dissolve in 100 cm^3 of water at 95°C?

34 If you have a certain amount of a solid to dissolve in water, you usually can hasten the process in various ways. Why do you think each of the following steps is effective in making the solid dissolve faster?

a) Stirring the water

b) Crushing the solid into smaller particles

c) Heating the water

 **Theme for a Short Essay**

Write an episode in a mystery centered on the possibility of selectively dissolving some substances mixed in with others. For example, a secret message written in ink may be covered by a painting. Describe real (not fictitious) substances.

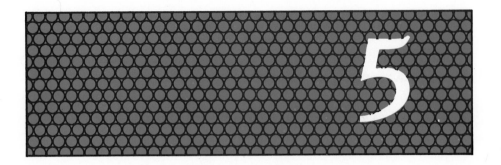

The Separation of Substances

In this chapter, we shall use the characteristic properties we have studied to work out a variety of methods for separating mixtures of different substances. These mixtures may be gases, liquids, or solids. By learning how to separate many kinds of mixtures, we also hope to come closer to understanding how simple substances are put together to form the many complex materials that are all around us. We shall start with a careful investigation of what happens when we distill a mixture of liquids.

5.1 EXPERIMENT FRACTIONAL DISTILLATION

In this experiment, you will determine some of the properties of a mixture of liquids. Then you will distill the mixture and examine the properties of the fractions to see if you succeeded in separating the liquids that made up the original mixture.

Part A

- Can you tell just by looking at it that the liquid is a mixture?

- Does the liquid have an odor?

Dip a small piece of paper in the liquid, and try lighting the 89 liquid on the paper with a match. Be sure to have a bucket with some water on your table in case the paper burns.

- Does the liquid burn?
- What is its density?
- Does sugar dissolve in the liquid?

Part B

Use the apparatus shown in Figure 5.1 to distill 5 cm³ of the mixture. Use a single collecting tube, and heat the liquid just enough to keep it boiling. Record the temperature of the *vapor* from the boiling liquid every half-minute while it distills. Continue to boil the liquid almost to dryness.

Make a graph of the boiling temperature as a function of the time.

- What do you conclude from your graph about the number of fractions you should collect to separate the different substances in the mixture?
- At what temperatures should you shift from one collecting tube to another?

Indicate on your graph the temperatures at which you decided to change collecting tubes.

Part C

Now fractionally distill about 25 cm³ of the liquid. Label the test tubes containing the fractions, so that you can keep track of them throughout the rest of the experiment. Test each of the fractions for odor and flammability.

Part D

- Does sugar dissolve in fraction 1?
- What is the density of fraction 1?

Distill the fraction into a single test tube, recording the boiling temperature every half-minute until the fraction has nearly boiled away. Draw a boiling-point graph for fraction 1.

Part E

Repeat *Part D* for each of the other fractions.

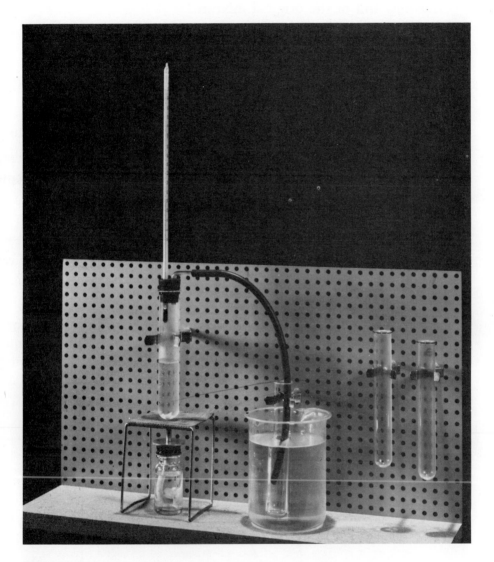

Figure 5.1

Apparatus for the fractional distillation of a liquid. The thermometer
bulb is close to the top of the test tube so that it measures the temperature of the vapor that condenses in the outlet tube. If there is more
than one liquid in the boiling mixture, most of the high-boiling-point
liquids will condense and flow back down the test-tube walls before
they reach the upper part of the test tube. The thermometer in this
apparatus is not used to measure the boiling temperature of the liquid, but serves to show when collecting tubes should be changed to
receive different fractions.

Part F

Summarize your findings, and compare the smell, flammability, density, ability to dissolve sugar, and boiling point of each of the fractions and of the original mixture.

- What do you conclude about the composition of the fractions?

- Can you identify the substances in the mixture? (See Table 3.2, page 65.)

- What other tests might you make to help identify these substances?

- What do you think would happen if you were to redistill each of the fractions separately into three fractions of equal volume?

1† In what characteristic property must two liquids differ before we can consider separating a mixture of them by fractional distillation?

2 The temperature-time graph shown in Figure A was made during the fractional distillation of a mixture of two liquids, E and F, and fractions were collected during the time intervals I, II, III, and IV. Liquid E has a higher boiling point than liquid F. What liquid or liquids were collected during each of the time intervals?

Figure A
For problem 2

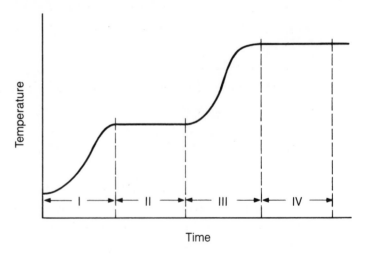

3 Carlos boiled a liquid and recorded the temperature at 1-minute intervals until the liquid had nearly boiled away. How do you explain the shape of the curve he got? (See Figure B.)

Figure B
For problem 3

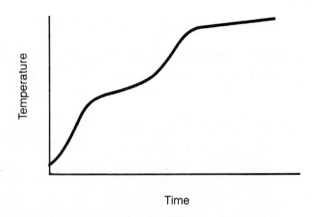

5.2 PETROLEUM

It is not always easy to separate a mixture of liquids into pure substances by fractional distillation. If the boiling points of the substances in a mixture are nearly the same, they will all boil off together. In a liquid mixture containing many substances, some are sure to have boiling points close together. When we distill such a mixture, each fraction we get is made up of a number of different substances whose boiling points are close together. The first part to condense in one fraction may contain some of the substances that condensed in the last part of the previous fraction. However, the fractions that are more widely separated in boiling range are less likely to contain the same substances. Petroleum is an example of such a mixture; the compositions of typical fractions distilled from petroleum are shown in Table 5.1.

Petroleum is believed to be produced naturally from animal and vegetable matter at the bottoms of shallow seas and swamps. When tiny plants and animals die in the sea, they settle slowly to the bottom, where they become trapped in mud and sand. This sediment of mud, sand, and dead organisms slowly becomes thicker and thicker. In a million years, it may become hundreds of meters deep. Such layers of sediment are very heavy, and the lower layers are compressed so much that they turn into rock layers. During this time, some of the body tissue of the entrapped organisms is changed into a viscous, sticky liquid that is a mixture of many thousands of different substances. This liquid is called "petroleum" or "crude oil." It is slowly squeezed out of the sediment in which it forms and eventually spreads through porous rock layers like water in a sponge.

Table 5.1   A Few of the Substances Found in Petroleum

Substance	Density at 0°C (g/cm³)	Freezing point (°C)	Boiling point (°C)	Common products of petroleum		
				fuel gas	gasoline	kerosene
Methane	7.16×10^{-4}	−182.5	−161	X		
Ethane	1.35×10^{-3}	−183	−88	X		
Propane	2.02×10^{-3}	−190	−43	X		
Butane	2.68×10^{-3}	−138	−0.5	X		
Pentane	0.626	−129	36			
Hexane	0.660	−94	69		X	
Heptane	0.684	−90	98		X	
Octane	0.703	−57	125		X	
Nonane	0.722	−51	151		X	X
Decane	0.730	−30	174		X	X
Undecane	0.741	−26	196			X
Dodecane	0.750	−10	216			X
Tridecane	0.755	−5.5	236			X
Tetradecane	0.765	5.5	254			X
Pentadecane	0.776	10	271			X
Hexadecane	0.773	18	287			X

There are many more substances in the above products and also in the higher-boiling-point fractions not listed in the table—fractions such as fuel oils, lubricating oils, waxes, asphalt, and coke (mostly carbon).

In the course of more millions of years, the ever-changing crust of the earth—buckling in some places, rising in others, and sinking in still others—slowly moves and compresses the rock layers that were on the ocean bottom. Sometimes the porous oil-bearing rock is covered by a layer of hard, nonporous rock that has been bent into a dome or arch, as shown in Figure 5.2. Then the oil will be trapped, and cannot by itself squeeze to the surface. If it were not trapped, much of it would wash away and be lost. Most of the petroleum in the earth's crust is stored by nature under formations of nonporous rock, which trap the liquids below them. As Figure 5.2 shows, natural gas (the low-boiling-point substances in petroleum) and salt water from the sea are often trapped along with the oil. The nonporous "cap rock" may be hundreds of meters thick. It is expensive and difficult to drill through all this rock to get to the petroleum below, and it is not easy to predict where oil is trapped. Deep and expensive wells often fail to reach oil or gas. Some wells produce nothing but salt water, whereas others remain dry.

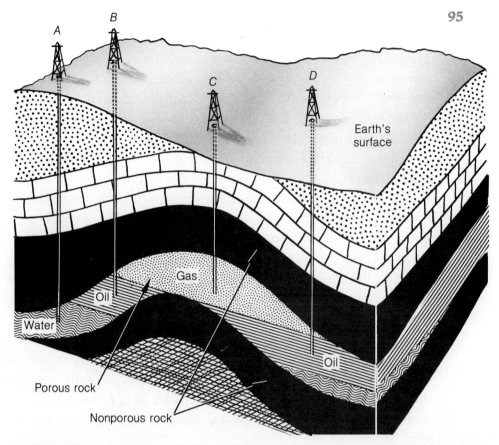

Figure 5.2

A cross section of the earth's crust, showing how oil and natural gas are trapped in a porous rock layer by nonporous rock layers above and below. Note that well *A* produces only water, and well *C* produces only gas.

Petroleum was first discovered where it seeped to the surface in shallow pools. Once exposed to the air, some of the lower-boiling-point substances slowly evaporated, leaving behind tarry, almost solid asphalt. These tars, as well as the liquid petroleum, were used for many of the same purposes in the ancient world as were the tars and watery substances obtained from the distillation of wood.

One of the ancient methods used to distill crude oil consisted of heating the oil in a copper urn with a wool "sponge" at the narrow mouth of the vessel. The vapors condensed in the sponge, which was squeezed out into containers from time to time. A variation of this method made use of a heavy wick of wool that led from the mouth of the urn into a collecting vessel. Such a wick was a crude form of condenser.

The widespread use of kerosene lamps a little over 100 years ago—and the more recent use of gasoline engines—created a new demand for petroleum. This led to improved methods of locating oil and drilling wells. Better equipment was also developed for fractionally distilling petroleum on a large scale.

A simplified diagram of this equipment, called a fractionating column, is shown in Figure 5.3. Heated crude oil enters the column near the bottom. The column contains a series of horizontal trays. As vapors from the heated liquid pass up through the column, the high-boiling-point substances condense in the lower, hotter trays. As the vapors move upward, they bubble through the liquid in the trays. In each tray, the condensing vapors increase the concentration of the substances whose boiling points are higher than the temperature of the tray. The rising vapors therefore become richer in the low-boiling substances. Some of the liquid that condenses in each tray overflows into the tray below, where it becomes heated again and redistills. Each tray thus boils a particular mixture at a particular temperature. The temperature of the trays and the boiling points of the substances in them decrease as one goes higher up the column.

The different fractions leave the column at different heights (Figure 5.3). Fractions with which you are familiar are gasoline, kerosene, diesel fuel, heating and lubricating oils, paraffin, and asphalt.

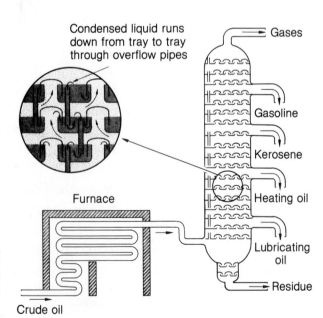

Figure 5.3
A simplified diagram of a fractionating column used in the fractional distillation of petroleum.

4 A sample of crude oil is boiled for several minutes. What change takes place in its density? (See Table 5.1.)

5.3 INDUSTRIAL DISTILLATION OF WOOD

You saw in Experiment 1 on the distillation of wood that liquids could be produced by heating wood strongly in the absence of air. To recover the maximum amount of commercially valuable substances, a different process is used. Such a process was developed about 80 years ago for utilizing the waste wood in pine-tree stumps. The process, with some improvements, is still in use today. Its success makes digging up pine-tree stumps and processing the wood profitable.

The stumps are ground up and shredded at the plant, and the shredded wood is loaded into a large cylindrical vessel called an extractor (Figure 5.4). There the wood is heated and mixed with a

Figure 5.4
The top of an extractor being loaded with shredded pine stump. Most of the vessel is below the floor on which the worker stands. (*Courtesy Newport Division, Reichold Chemicals, Inc.*)

petroleum solvent—usually one whose properties lie between those of gasoline and kerosene. The solvent dissolves the desired substances contained in the wood. After some intermediate stages, the resulting solution passes through a fractionating column (Figure 5.5).

The principal products of the process are turpentine, dipentene, and pine oil, together with the petroleum solvent, which is used over again in the extractors. Some of the products are used directly, some are only the starting point of the manufacture of many other substances used in the chemical industry. Pine oil has a household use in disinfectants and cleaners. Among many other applications, it is often used in ore flotation (see section 5.4). Turpentine has long been used as a paint thinner. It is also used in the manufacture of adhesives, coatings, pesticides, and other materials.

Figure 5.5
A general view of a fractionating column used in the processing of pine stumps. (*Courtesy Newport Division, Reichold Chemicals, Inc.*)

5 Suggest a reason why stump wood is shredded before being loaded into the extractors.

6 Suggest a reason why the petroleum solvent is heated in the extractors.

5.4 THE SEPARATION OF INSOLUBLE SOLIDS

Solids with a density greater than that of water sink in water, and those with a lesser density float, provided they are insoluble (section 3.9). We can use this fact to separate a mixture of sawdust and sand. After stirring the mixture in water, we can skim off the floating sawdust. Then we can pour off the water and dry the sand.

This method is called separation by flotation and is widely used in industry to concentrate ores (Figure 5.6). For example, a common copper ore, copper sulfide, is usually found mixed with

Figure 5.6
Three flotation tanks at a copper plant. (*Arizona Photographic Associates, Inc.*)

large amounts of worthless rock. The ore is finely ground, and then mixed with water and selected reagents. This mixture is agitated violently with air to produce a heavy foam. The copper sulfide is contained in the floating foam; the ground rock settles. The foam is removed, and the copper sulfide is recovered.

5.5   EXPERIMENT   SEPARATION OF A MIXTURE OF SOLIDS

Examine the mixture of solids supplied by your teacher. If one solid is soluble in water and the other is not, you can separate them eas-

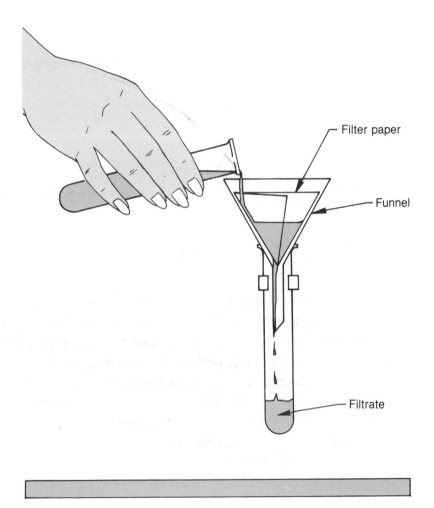

Figure 5.7
Filtering a liquid. The filter paper is folded into a cone, which fits snugly into the funnel.

ily by dissolving one and separating it from the other by filtering. You can do this in the following way: Put about 1.5 g of the mixture into a test tube, and add 5 cm³ of water. Stopper the test tube, and shake it for several minutes.

- Do you think either substance dissolved?

To find out, filter out the undissolved material, as shown in Figure 5.7. Wash the precipitate left on the filter paper by pouring an additional 10 cm³ of water into the funnel. You can now put about 5 cm³ of the clear liquid—the filtrate—into an evaporating dish and boil it to dryness.

- Have the two substances been separated?

7† In what characteristic property must two solids differ if they are to be separated merely by being dissolved at room temperature and filtered?

8 Much salt is obtained from salt mines, in which great masses of salt occur mixed with insoluble earthy impurities. What steps can be taken to purify the salt?

9 How could drinking water be obtained from seawater?

5.6 THE SEPARATION OF A MIXTURE OF SOLUBLE SOLIDS

In the previous experiment, you were able to separate two solids because one of them was soluble in water and the other was not. Suppose that you have a mixture containing 5 g of sodium chloride and 5 g of potassium nitrate. Both of these substances readily dissolve in water. In fact, as you see from Figure 5.8, at room temperature they have nearly the same solubility. Therefore, if we completely dissolve the 5 g of potassium nitrate in water, at room temperature, all of the sodium chloride will also dissolve. How can these substances be separated?

Figure 5.8 shows that the solubility of sodium chloride hardly changes with temperature, whereas the solubility of potassium nitrate rises sharply with temperature. We can make use of the effect of temperature on the solubility of these two substances to separate them.

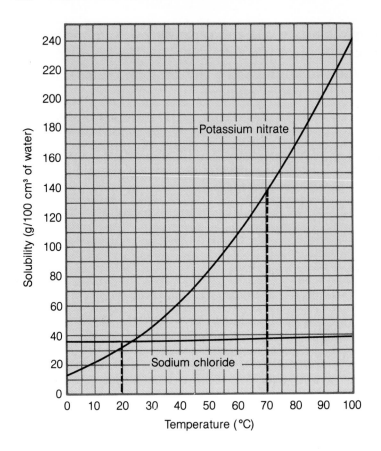

Figure 5.8
Solubility curves of sodium chloride and potassium nitrate.

Note that at 70°C, for example, 138 g of potassium nitrate will dissolve in 100 cm³ of water. Therefore, the amount of water needed to dissolve completely only 5.0 g of potassium nitrate at this temperature is 100 cm³ × 5.0 g/138 g = 3.6 cm³.

How much sodium chloride will dissolve in 3.6 cm³ of water at 70°C? To answer this question, first note from Figure 5.8 that 38 g of sodium chloride will dissolve in 100 cm³ of water at 70°C. Therefore, only 38 g × 3.6 cm³/100 cm³ = 1.4 g of sodium chloride will dissolve in 3.6 cm³ of water.

Thus, if we add a mixture of 5.0 g of potassium nitrate and 5.0 g sodium chloride to 3.6 cm³ of water, all the potassium nitrate and a small amount of sodium chloride will dissolve at 70°C. Most of the sodium chloride will remain as a solid at the bottom of the test tube. Therefore, filtering the hot solution will leave most of the sodium chloride on the filter paper. The solution that passes through the filter paper will contain all the potassium nitrate and some sodium chloride.

What will happen if we let the filtered solution cool to room temperature? Referring again to Figure 5.8, we see that practically all of the dissolved sodium chloride and some potassium nitrate will remain in the solution. However, most of the potassium nitrate will precipitate out as a solid and can then be separated from the solution by filtration. This process is summarized in Figure 5.9.

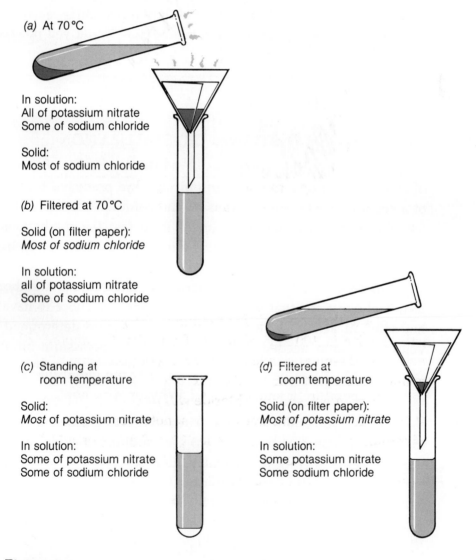

(a) At 70 °C

In solution:
All of potassium nitrate
Some of sodium chloride

Solid:
Most of sodium chloride

(b) Filtered at 70 °C

Solid (on filter paper):
Most of sodium chloride

In solution:
all of potassium nitrate
Some of sodium chloride

(c) Standing at
    room temperature

Solid:
Most of potassium nitrate

In solution:
Some of potassium nitrate
Some of sodium chloride

(d) Filtered at
    room temperature

Solid (on filter paper):
Most of potassium nitrate

In solution:
Some potassium nitrate
Some sodium chloride

Figure 5.9
A diagram of the series of steps for separating a mixture of equal masses of sodium chloride and potassium nitrate.

10 a) How much sodium chloride does not dissolve in the 3.6 cm^3 of water at 70°C in Experiment 5.6?
b) How much sodium chloride remains in solution after cooling to room temperature?
c) How much solid sodium chloride is recovered at the end of the experiment?

11 a) How much potassium nitrate remains in solution at room temperature at the end of the separation?
b) How much potassium nitrate can be recovered in solid form?

12 Suppose you wish to separate more of the two solids remaining in solution at the end of the experiment. How would you proceed to do this?

5.7   EXPERIMENT   FRACTIONAL CRYSTALLIZATION

In the preceding section, we considered the separation of a mixture of sodium chloride and potassium nitrate. We predicted the results of a separation procedure based on the solubility curves in Figure 5.8. The purpose of *this* experiment is to test the predictions by using the same quantities of solids and water as determined in the preceding section.

Before you begin the experiment, there are a number of technical questions that you should consider. We chose to have the hot solution at 70°C. This choice of temperature determined the volume of water needed to dissolve all of the potassium nitrate.

• Must you be sure when you filter the liquid that its temperature is indeed 70°C? Why or why not?

After you add 3.6 cm^3 of water to the 10-g mixture of solids (5.0 g of potassium nitrate and 5.0 g of sodium chloride), heat the mixture while stirring it, and then filter.

A hot solution cools rapidly. To prevent this, you can preheat the funnel, filter paper, and the test tube in which you will collect the filtrate by rinsing them with hot water.

• What do you expect to have on the filter paper?

• What substance do you expect to precipitate from the filtrate?

When solids precipitate slowly out of the solution, the crystals they form have characteristic shapes.

- What is the shape of the crystals that precipitated from the solution when it cooled?

The sodium chloride that you separated in your experiment was never dissolved. To observe its crystals, you can prepare a saturated solution of it and allow it to evaporate overnight.

- What is the shape of the sodium chloride crystals?

- Is there another way, other than by observing the crystal shapes, that you could show that the two solids you separated are different?

---

13 a) If a solution containing 40 g of potassium nitrate in 100 cm³ of water at 100°C is cooled to 25°C, how much potassium nitrate will precipitate out of solution? (See Figure 5.8.)
b) Suppose that the 40 g of potassium nitrate is dissolved in only 50 cm³ of water at 100°C. How much potassium nitrate will precipitate out if the solution is cooled to 25°C?

14 Suppose you dissolve 30 g of sodium chloride in 100 cm³ of water at 100°C and boil away 50 cm³ of the water.
a) How many grams of sodium chloride will remain in solution?
b) How many grams will precipitate out of solution?

15 Suppose you dissolve 40 g of potassium nitrate in 100 cm³ of water at 100°C.
a) If half the solution is poured out, how many grams of potassium nitrate will the remaining solution contain?
b) Now, instead of pouring out part of the solution, you boil away 50 cm³ of water. How many grams of potassium nitrate will remain in solution at 100°C?
c) If the solution remaining in (b) were cooled to 25°C, how much potassium nitrate would precipitate out of solution?

5.8 EXPERIMENT PAPER CHROMATOGRAPHY

Try filtering some black ink. Is there any evidence that ink is a mixture?

Completely distill about 5 cm³ of ink.

- Is the ink made up of more than one substance?

You probably saw evidence, when you filtered the ink, that would lead you to believe that there are several substances of different colors in the ink. The colored fringe that you saw about the black region on the filter paper indicates that substances in the ink move at different speeds across the filter paper. We shall now try to separate these substances from the liquid, using a long strip of filter paper.

Hang a strip of filter paper streaked with ink in a graduate containing water, as shown in Figure 5.10. When the color has risen up the paper to about 2 or 3 cm below the top, remove the paper and hang it up to dry.

- How many different substances can you identify?

- Can you put the substances back together again and make black ink?

Cut out each of the colored sections, and put each one in a separate test tube. Add between $\frac{1}{2}$ and 1 cm^3 of water to each tube.

- Do the colored substances dissolve?

Pour the liquids from all three test tubes together into one test tube.

- What color do you get?

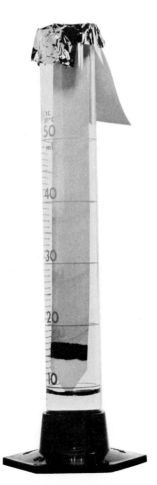

Figure 5.10
One method of making a paper chromatograph of black ink. The point of the filter-paper strip extends into the water so that the ink streak is about 1 cm above the water. The strip is held in place by an aluminum-foil cover bent over the top. The walls of the graduate should be dry, so that the paper will come in contact with water only from the bottom.

5.9   MIXTURES OF GASES: NITROGEN AND OXYGEN

In this chapter, we have seen how we can separate mixtures of liquids, mixtures of solids and liquids, and mixtures of solids. We have not yet considered the separation of mixtures of gases. If we have a gas dissolved in a liquid, all we have to do is heat the mixture. (You did this in section 4.12, when you heated a solution of ammonia gas in water.) When a glass of cold water warms up to room temperature, bubbles of air dissolved in the water appear, sticking to the sides of the glass. If we warm the water further, more air bubbles appear, and some rise to the top long before we reach the temperature at which water boils. Separating mixtures of gases alone, however, requires different methods from those we have used in experiments so far.

Mixtures of gases are very common. Table 5.1 (page 94) lists four gases that are mixed together in the petroleum fraction called "fuel gas."

There are a number of ways to separate gases. One of them, which is widely used, is to cool the mixture until it condenses to form a liquid. Then we can make use of the different boiling points of the various liquids and fractionally distill the cold liquid. The gases are thus collected one by one, as the boiling temperature levels off at new plateaus.

If we liquefy air and fractionally distill it in this way, we find that air separates mainly into two fractions: A glowing splint bursts into a bright flame when placed in one of them, but even a splint that is burning goes out when placed in the other. Neither gas turns limewater milky. The gas that causes the glowing splint to burst into flame is called "oxygen"; the one that does not is "nitrogen." These two gases together make up about 99 percent of the gases in air. Nitrogen makes up about 80 percent of the atmosphere, and oxygen about 20 percent. The densities, melting points, and boiling points of nitrogen and oxygen are given in Table 5.2.

Table 5.2

Gas	Density (g/cm³)	Melting point (°C)	Boiling point (°C)
Nitrogen	1.2×10^{-3}	−210	−196
Oxygen	1.3×10^{-3}	−218	−183

The densities are given for atmospheric pressure and room temperature.

The cheapest way of obtaining oxygen and nitrogen is to condense air into a liquid and then fractionally distill it. Most of the oxygen and nitrogen commercially manufactured is produced by this method.

16 How could you separate ammonia gas from air?

5.10 LOW TEMPERATURES

The melting points and boiling points given in Table 5.2 are far below any temperature you can reach in your laboratory. How is it possible to cool things to such low temperatures?

One method of cooling gases depends on the fact that very highly compressed gases cool when allowed to expand. Figure 5.11 shows how this effect can be used to cool air to temperatures low enough to liquefy it. Air at very high pressure and room temperature flows down the long tube in the center and escapes through a small opening at the bottom. As it escapes, it expands and cools. When the flow is first started, the escaping air does not cool enough to condense into liquid air; but as this escaping cold air flows up past the long tube, it cools the air moving down inside the tube.

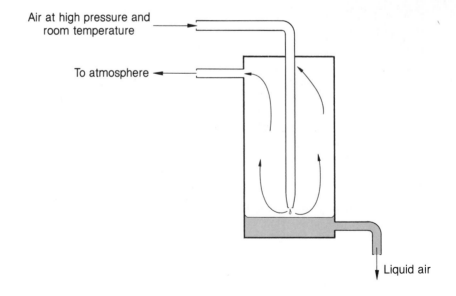

Figure 5.11
A simplified diagram showing the essential steps in liquefying air.

Thus, when the air inside escapes at the bottom, it is already cold and cools off still more on expansion. After the apparatus has run for some time, the expanding air cools enough so that some of it condenses into liquid and collects at the bottom of the apparatus. Of course, the whole apparatus shown in the figure must be well insulated to keep the inside cold. Actual liquid-air machines are more complicated than this simplified diagram shows, but many of them operate on this principle.

It is one thing to produce very low temperatures, but another to measure them. The usual way of calibrating a liquid thermometer is to mark on the stem the liquid levels when the thermometer is placed in melting ice and then in boiling water. These temperatures are labeled 0°C and 100°C. The scale is then marked off into 100 equal divisions between the points, each division representing 1°C. If we specify the liquid used—mercury, for example—we have then defined a temperature scale. Many liquids behave the same way between 0°C and 100°C. For example, two thermometers calibrated in this way, one containing mercury and the other toluene, will both read very nearly the same temperature when they are placed together in water at any temperature between 0°C and 100°C.

If we extend the temperature scale on a calibrated liquid thermometer by marking equal divisions below 0°C, we still find very close agreement between thermometers containing different liquids, such as mercury and toluene. This agreement continues until very low temperatures are reached, where we run into trouble. Substances that are liquids between 0°C and 100°C solidify at some lower temperature.

However, gases also expand and contract with temperature changes. Many of them do not condense until they are extremely cold, and we can use them in thermometers to measure very low temperatures. A simple gas thermometer is shown in Figure 5.12. If

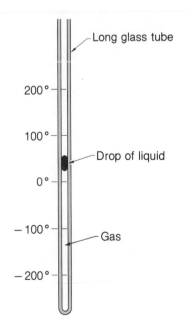

Figure 5.12
A simple gas thermometer calibrated in degrees Celsius.

we calibrate it the same way we calibrate a liquid thermometer, we find that it will give the same temperature readings as will a standard liquid thermometer. This is true of nearly all gas thermometers. Furthermore, at very low temperatures, where thermometers containing various liquids freeze, most gas thermometers containing different gases continue to agree closely. Thus, gas thermometers extend our temperature scale. To measure the freezing point of oxygen, we need a gas that condenses below −218°C. Helium boils at −269°C and is used in gas thermometers.

5.11   MIXTURES AND PURE SUBSTANCES

In this chapter, we have found ways to separate different substances from each other by using characteristic properties. We learned that a difference in density can be used to separate two solids; that solids can also be separated by differences in solubility; and that a difference in the boiling points of different liquids enables us to separate them by fractional distillation.

Suppose we experiment with a piece of solid material to see if we can separate it into two or more substances. First we grind it up and mix it with water, stirring it thoroughly. We observe that some particles of a yellowish solid float on the surface, while particles of a gray solid sink to the bottom. We skim off the floating material, whose density is obviously less than that of water. We dry it, call it fraction 1, and set it aside. Then we filter the water and the more dense solid that is in the bottom of the test tube. This solid, which remains on the filter paper, we dry, label fraction 2, and set aside also. We know that these two solids, fractions 1 and 2, are different substances, because they have different densities.

We now test the filtrate to see if any material has dissolved in the water. Evaporating away the water, we find a small amount of white solid. This substance is different from both fractions 1 and 2 because it is soluble in water, and we call it fraction 3. The whole process of the separation of three fractions from a piece of solid material is diagramed in Figure 5.13.

We now have separated out three different substances, but perhaps each of these can be further separated. To find out, we use other separation methods. We may, for example, try to melt and even fractionally distill each of the fractions, or we may try dissolv-

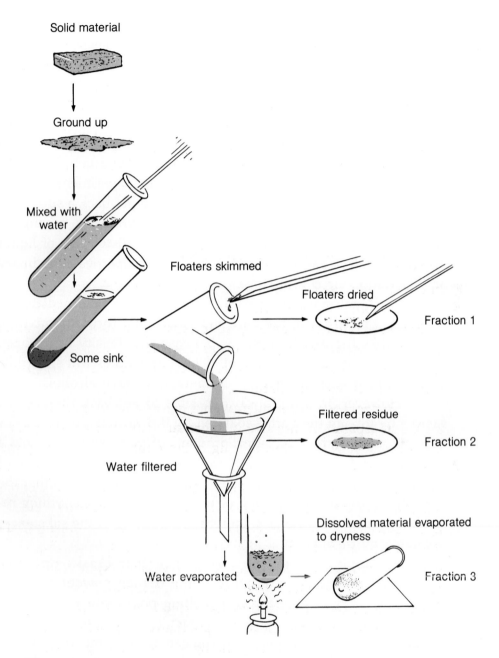

Solid material

Ground up

Mixed with water

Some sink

Floaters skimmed

Floaters dried

Fraction 1

Water filtered

Filtered residue

Fraction 2

Dissolved material evaporated to dryness

Water evaporated

Fraction 3

Figure 5.13
A diagram of an example of the series of steps for separating three fractions obtained from a ground-up solid.

ing them in different liquids. Suppose that boiling, melting, and mixing with alcohol and other liquids do not produce anything with characteristic properties different from those of the three fractions we have already found. By using all these various tools of separation again and again, we find that the characteristic properties of our three fractions remain unaltered. We call such substances whose properties are not changed by repeating any of these procedures "pure" substances.

Suppose we mix together all the pure substances that we obtain in this way and get back a material that has the same characteristic properties as the original sample. We can say that the original sample was a *mixture* of the pure substances. For example, if you mixed all the fractions you separated in your experiment on fractional distillation (Experiment 5.1), you would get back a substance that has the same properties you started with. Similarly, mixing together the various fractions obtained from the distillation of liquid air would yield a gas with exactly the same properties as ordinary air. Therefore, air is a mixture.

Note that many properties of a mixture are intermediate between the properties of the pure substances that form the mixture. For example, the density of air is between the density of nitrogen and that of oxygen. A mixture of alcohol and water will smell like alcohol, but it will only burn if it contains enough alcohol.

However, it is not always possible to get back the original sample by mixing the parts separated by the various processes. For example, mixing the distillation products of petroleum will yield a liquid similar but not identical to the original sample. You know, of course, from your own experience that you cannot mix together the products of the dry distillation of wood and get back anything resembling wood. Wood is not, therefore, a mixture of the substances separated by distillation.

A simple example of a substance that breaks up when heated and that is not a mixture is the orange powder mercuric oxide. If you try to determine its melting point, you will discover that when it is heated, it gives off a gas. You can test this gas and find it to be oxygen. Furthermore, you can detect some droplets of a silvery liquid—mercury—in the test tube. Mixing the oxygen and the mercury together, however, will not give back the mercuric oxide. The two components remain separated as a gas and a silvery liquid.

Mercuric oxide is a pure substance that cannot be separated into simpler substances by most of the methods we used to separate mixtures. When it is separated by heating, it cannot be put back together simply by mixing.

17 Suppose you mixed together all the fractions you obtained from the fractional distillation of the liquid in Experiment 5.1. What do you think would be the properties of this liquid?

18 The substances you obtained by distilling wood (Experiment 1.1), when mixed together, will not give anything like wood—even ground-up, finely powdered wood. What does this tell you about the substances in wood as compared with the substances you obtained in the distillation?

For Home, Desk, and Lab

19 In earlier times, people would search out sandy stream beds in which small particles of gold were mixed with the sand. They separated this gold from the sand by "panning." Find out how this was done. What characteristic property of the substances made panning possible?

20 Figure 5.2 shows four oil wells drilled into oil-bearing porous rock. Can you suggest some method, other than drilling deeper, for getting more oil from well D after the oil level drops below the end of the well?

21 a) In Table 5.1 (page 94), which fractions would be liquid at room temperature (20°C)? Which would be solids? Which would be gases?
b) You can see from the table that pentane is not an ingredient in any of the common products listed. How can you account for this?

22 Using the data in Table 5.1 (page 94), draw and label a possible distillation curve for a mixture of hexane, nonane, and tetradecane.

23 When ethanol is to be used for industrial or commercial purposes other than as a beverage, it is customarily "denatured"; that is, a small quantity of another substance is added to it so that it is unfit for use as a beverage. What, in general, do you think some of the properties of the added substance might be?

24 How would you separate a mixture of powdered sugar and powdered citric acid?

25 The mineral called "Gay-Lussite" appears to be a pure substance, but it is actually a mixture composed of calcium carbonate (limestone), sodium carbonate (soda ash), and water. Describe how you would go about separating these three substances from the rock. Some properties of calcium carbonate and sodium carbonate are listed in the following table.

Property	Calcium carbonate	Sodium carbonate
Melting point	Decomposes at 825°C	851°C
Solubility in alcohol	Insoluble	Insoluble
Solubility in hydro-chloric acid	Soluble	Soluble
Solubility in water	Insoluble	7 g/100 cm³ at 0°C; 45 g/100 cm³ at 100°C

26 If you have 100 cm³ of water at 100°C, saturated with both potassium nitrate and sodium chloride, what happens if the temperature is lowered to 10°C? (Refer to Figure 5.8, and assume that the solubility curves of these substances are the same as in the figure, even when they are dissolved together.)

27 You can use paper chromatography to separate the components in many common substances. Try this technique with any of the following substances you can find at home: tomato paste, different colors and brands of ink, the coloring in leaves and vegetables (grind the leaves first in alcohol), and flower petals.

28 Chlorophyll can be extracted from leaves by grinding them with alcohol to give a dark-green solution. By careful application of paper chromatography, bands of yellow and red color, as well as green bands, can be detected. What other reason do you have to suspect the presence of substances producing these colors in leaves? Why don't you ordinarily see them?

29 As liquid air boils away, the remaining liquid becomes richer in one of the two gases—nitrogen or oxygen. Which one is it? How do you know?

30 a) How would you calibrate the simple gas thermometer shown in Figure 5.12 to read in degrees Celsius?
     b) Which end of the liquid drop would you take as a reference point?

31 What would you do to separate (a) alcohol from water, (b) sodium chloride from sodium nitrate, and (c) nitrogen from oxygen?

32 A sample of a liquid was boiled for 12 minutes. During that time, the boiling point remained constant, and the volume was reduced to half. Is the liquid a pure substance?

33 Suppose you had a mixture of sand and salt in a small box.
a) How could you separate these substances?
b) How would you determine the ratio of the mass of sand to the mass of salt?
c) If you were mixing sand and salt together, what mass ratios would it be possible for you to make?

Theme for a Short Essay

You devoted several hours to the "sludge test." Do you think this test is a good way to assess your progress in this course? Why, or why not? Include enough information about the test so that a friend who has never heard about the "sludge test" will be able to understand your reasoning.

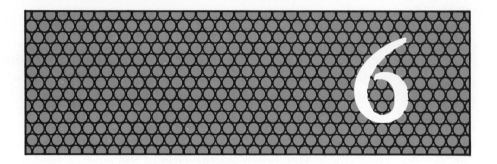

Compounds

At the end of the last chapter, we mentioned a pure substance, mercuric oxide, that can be broken down into two different pure substances—mercury and oxygen—by heating. The properties of these two components are quite different from those of mercuric oxide. Furthermore, the mercury and oxygen cannot be put back together to form mercuric oxide simply by mixing. In the next two sections, you will use two different experimental methods to study other examples of breaking down pure substances.

6.1 EXPERIMENT DECOMPOSITION OF SODIUM CHLORATE

What happens when you place about 5 g of sodium chlorate in a test tube and heat it with two alcohol burners, as shown in Figure 6.1? (**CAUTION:** Be sure to use a glass-wool plug and a test tube that is clean and dry.) The apparatus is arranged so that you can collect several test tubes of whatever gas is given off. When you have filled two or three test tubes with gas, take the stopper out of the test tube you are heating. This ensures that no water will be accidentally sucked back into the hot tube. A glowing splint may help you to identify the gas.

To make sure that all the solid in the test tube has been
116 heated thoroughly, continue to heat the material for about 10 min-

Figure 6.1
Apparatus for decomposing sodium chlorate and collecting any gas
that is given off. The glass-wool plug in the top of the test tube prevents the sodium chlorate from spattering up and coming into contact
with the stopper.

utes after no further change is observed. You may want to rotate the
tube to do this, but don't burn your fingers.

- Does the material left in the test tube have the same melting point as the material you started with?

- How does the solubility in water of the solid remaining in
  the test tube compare with the solubility of the sodium
  chlorate?

- What do you conclude from this experiment about what
  happens when sodium chlorate is heated?

- Can you get back the sodium chlorate by mixing the gas
  and the remaining solid?

———————————

It is not possible from the tests you have made in this experiment to identify the substance left in the test tube. More experi-

ments must be performed. One of those that is most useful is the determination of the solubility of the substance as a function of temperature.

To perform this test, a saturated solution (in water) of the substance remaining in the test tube was made at 100°C. Approximately 5 g of this hot solution was poured into a previously massed evaporating dish. When the solution had cooled to 80°C, another

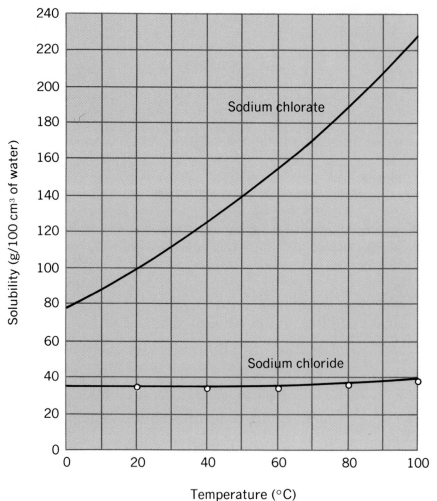

Figure 6.2
The circles on the graph are data points obtained by measuring the solubility of the solid that remained after the sodium chlorate was decomposed. The line labeled sodium chloride is the solubility curve of sodium chloride shown in Figure 4.3. The curve labeled sodium chlorate is included for comparison.

portion of solution was poured into a second evaporating dish, leaving behind all precipitated solid. This process was continued, with solution being poured off at 60°C, 40°C, and 20°C.

The concentration of the saturated solution in each dish was determined by using the same procedure as in Experiment 4.1. Each dish of saturated solution was accurately massed. Then the solution was evaporated to dryness with an alcohol burner, and the mass of solid was determined.

The mass of the water that evaporated was calculated from the difference in the mass of the saturated solution and of the solid. From these data, the solubility of each sample was calculated. After converting the data to g/100 cm³ of water, the solubilities were plotted, as shown in Figure 6.2. Note that the data points lie close to the solubility curve for sodium chloride. They certainly do not fit the solubility curve for sodium chlorate, which also is shown on the graph. It thus seems very likely that the solid resulting from heating sodium chlorate is sodium chloride. Sodium chlorate, a pure substance, can be decomposed into two pure substances. These have entirely different characteristic properties from those of the compound sodium chlorate.

---

1 Suppose that in decomposing sodium chlorate, you did not heat the sodium chlorate long enough to decompose all of it.
   a) What substances would be left in the test tube?
   b) How would you separate them?

6.2   EXPERIMENT   DECOMPOSITION OF WATER

Water is one of the pure substances we have separated out of many mixtures. But we have been unable to separate water itself into other substances by the methods we have used in the previous chapter. After heating, distilling, and freezing water, we always end up with plain water. To separate it into simpler substances, we shall need a new method, different from any we have used so far. Such a method, first used at the beginning of the nineteenth century, makes use of electricity.

Figure 6.3
Apparatus for decomposing water. The electrodes are clamped alongside the inverted test tubes and connected to a battery. Any gas that forms on either of the stainless-steel electrode tips will be collected when it rises and displaces water from its test tube. No reaction is observed until a small amount of sodium carbonate solution is added to the water.

Set up the apparatus shown in Figure 6.3. Connect the wires to the battery and see if anything happens. Since this reaction is very slow when only pure water is used, it is necessary to add something to speed up the process. Try adding from 10 to 30 cm³ of sodium carbonate solution to the water.

Disconnect the battery when one of the test tubes is nearly full of gas, and mark the volume of gas in each tube with a grease pencil or rubber band. You have probably heard that water is made up of hydrogen and oxygen. Test the gases to see if you come to the same conclusion. Be sure to remove the test tubes from the water in such a way that you do not lose the gases you wish to test.

Measure the volumes of the gases in the test tubes. To compare these two volumes, divide the volume of the hydrogen by the volume of the oxygen. This gives you the ratio of the volume of hydrogen to the volume of oxygen. Compare your ratio with the ratios obtained by students who used different amounts of sodium carbonate solution mixed with the water.

- Does the amount of solution added to the water affect the volume ratio?

- What is the mass ratio of hydrogen to oxygen?

A pure substance that can be broken up into two or more pure substances is called a "compound." The characteristic properties of a compound are quite different from those of its components.

2   In decomposing water, suppose you had filled many test tubes with gas, adding water to the beaker as it disappeared, but never adding more sodium carbonate. You would always have found the ratio of hydrogen to oxygen produced to be constant. What does this tell you about the source of the gases? About the sodium carbonate?

3† a) What is the total mass of oxygen and hydrogen that can be produced by the decomposition of 180 g of water by electrolysis?
    b) If all the hydrogen produced were burned in the air to form water, what mass of water would result?

4† Two test tubes contain equal volumes of gas at atmospheric pressure. If one contains oxygen and the other helium, is the mass of gas in both tubes the same?

5   From your data in Experiment 6.2, calculate the ratio of the mass of oxygen produced to the mass of hydrogen produced. How does your ratio compare with those found by other members of your class?

6.3   THE SYNTHESIS OF WATER

In the last experiment, you could have mixed oxygen and hydrogen gas together in a test tube. Nothing would have happened unless you had ignited the mixture. Then a violent reaction would have occurred. With the proper equipment, the gases could have been separated before ignition by cooling them down until the oxygen condensed at $-183°C$, leaving the hydrogen as a gas. But this method would not have worked if the mixture of gases had first been ignited. As a result of the ignition, the two gases would have combined to form a compound, water vapor, which cannot be separated into hydrogen or oxygen by condensation. The combining of substances to form a compound is called "synthesis." This process is the opposite of decomposition.

When you electrolyzed water, you found the ratio of the volume of hydrogen to the volume of oxygen produced. No matter how much water you decomposed, the ratio remained the same. Of course, you might have expected this, since all the water you used came from the same source. But can we combine hydrogen and oxygen in different proportions, or will they combine only in the same volume ratio?

To answer this question, we could try adding different volumes of hydrogen to a fixed volume of oxygen, igniting each mix-

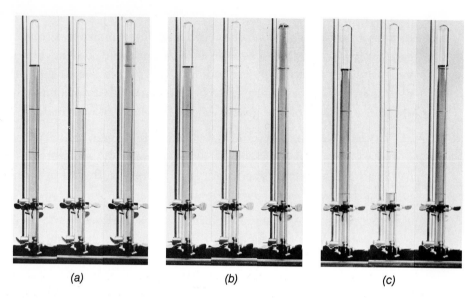

(a)   (b)   (c)

Figure 6.4

The photograph on the left in (*a*) shows a glass tube, originally filled with water, after a volume *V* of oxygen was bubbled into the bottom of the tube. The middle photograph shows the same tube after the same volume *V* of hydrogen was added to the oxygen. The photograph on the right shows the tube after the mixture was ignited by an electric spark through the gas. Note that a considerable amount of gas remains unreacted.

In (*b*) we see the same experiment shown in part (*a*), except that the volume of hydrogen used was 2*V*. Note that all of both gases reacted except for a small bubble at the top. The volume of this bubble is no greater than the experimental error in filling the tube.

In (*c*) the volume of hydrogen used was 3*V*. As in (*a*), a considerable volume of gas remains unreacted.

ture, and measuring how much of each gas, if any, remains uncombined.

We have done this experiment. First we filled a special shock-resistant glass tube with water and inverted it in a tray of water. A volume *V* of oxygen was then bubbled into the bottom of the tube. The oxygen rose to the top as shown in the photograph at the left in Figure 6.4(*a*). (The water levels are marked by rubber bands.)

We then added the same volume *V* of hydrogen to the tube (see the middle photograph in part (*a*) of Figure 6.4). Next, we ignited the mixture of gases by sending an electric spark through the mixture. After ignition, a considerable amount of gas remained unreacted, as shown by the photograph on the right in Figure 6.4(*a*).

Table 6.1

Tube	Initial volume of oxygen (cm³)	Initial volume of hydrogen (cm³)	Final volume of gas (cm³)	Volume of oxygen V_O that combined (cm³)	Volume of hydrogen V_H that combined (cm³)	Ratio V_H/V_O
1	25	25	12.4 oxygen	12.6	25	1.98
2	25	50	0.8	25	49.2	1.97
3	25	75	24.6 hydrogen	25	50.4	2.02

Figure 6.4(*b*) shows the same experiment repeated. This time the volume of hydrogen used was 2*V*, or twice the volume of oxygen. In this case, practically all of the mixture reacted. (Only a very small bubble of gas remained unreacted.)

In the experiment shown in Figure 6.4(*c*), the volume of hydrogen in the tube before ignition was 3*V*. A considerable amount of gas did not react.

From Figure 6.4, you can see that the ratios of the volumes of hydrogen to oxygen before ignition in (*a*), (*b*), and (*c*) were 1/1, 2/1, and 3/1, respectively. When tested after ignition, the gas remaining in (*a*) was oxygen and that in (*c*) was hydrogen. (The volume of the bubble remaining in (*b*) was too small to identify the gas.) The increased amount of water in the tubes came from the tray of water. The water produced in the reactions amounted to only a few drops.

The results of this experiment are shown in Figure 6.4 and Table 6.1. As you can see, the ratio of the volume of hydrogen to the volume of oxygen that combined to form water was the same in each case, regardless of the ratio of the volumes of the two gases in the mixture before they were ignited.

This is the ratio of hydrogen gas to oxygen gas obtained by the careful electrolysis of water in Experiment 6.2. The experiment in Figure 6.4 shows that over the range of volumes used, if the volume of either gas was greater than that needed for a ratio of 2, only part of the gas reacted. The excess remained uncombined.

6† If 18 g of water is decomposed into hydrogen and oxygen by electrolysis, 16 g of oxygen and 2 g of hydrogen are produced. Using the table of densities in Chapter 3 (page 63), find (a) the volume of water decomposed and (b) the volume of hydrogen produced.

7   You mix 100 cm³ of oxygen with 200 cm³ of hydrogen. The volumes of both gases are measured at atmospheric pressure and at room temperature.
   a)   Calculate the mass of oxygen and the mass of hydrogen used.
   b)   If you ignited the mixture, what mass of water would result from the reaction?
   c)   What volume of water would be produced?

8   If in problem 7 you had used 100 cm³ of oxygen but only 50 cm³ of hydrogen, what mass of water would have resulted?

9†   Three tubes are filled with a mixture of hydrogen and oxygen in a manner similar to that used in Figure 6.4. If the three tubes contain the following volumes of hydrogen and oxygen, what is the volume of the unreacted gas remaining in each tube after they are ignited?

Tube	Volume of oxygen (cm³)	Volume of hydrogen (cm³)
I	25	75
II	50	50
III	25	50

6.4   EXPERIMENT   SYNTHESIS OF ZINC CHLORIDE

You have learned that hydrogen and oxygen combine in a definite ratio, no matter how much of each we mix together and ignite. In that case, the reaction involves two gases. Let us now investigate what happens when we dissolve a metal in an acid: in this case, zinc in hydrochloric acid.

Everyone in your class will use the same amount of hydrochloric acid, but different groups will add different amounts of zinc. When the reaction is complete, you will determine the mass of zinc that reacted. You will then evaporate the remaining liquid and mass the solid residue. Then each group will calculate the ratio it found for the mass of zinc reacted to the mass of solid product formed (the solid is called "zinc chloride").

The reaction between the zinc and the acid will produce much heat. To keep the mixture cool, you can perform the reaction in a large test tube placed in a beaker of cold water. (Figure 6.5.)

Mass out an exact amount of the zinc somewhere between 0.5 g and 4 g. Place the zinc in the test tube, and add 10 cm³ of hy-

Figure 6.5
Zinc is dissolved in 10 cm³ of hydrochloric acid in a test tube, which is
placed in a beaker of cold water to keep the solution from getting too
hot.

drochloric acid. **CAUTION:** Be careful not to get any of the solution on your books or clothes. If some acid spills on your hands,
wash them thoroughly with water.

* What is the gas given off in the reaction?

The reaction at first is quite vigorous. However, to make sure
that it is complete, allow the mixture of zinc and acid to stand overnight. In the next period, pour the liquid from the test tube into an
evaporating dish that you have already massed. If there is still zinc
left over from the reaction, pour the solution so that the solid stays
in the test tube. Wash the test tube, and any zinc remaining, with
5 cm³ of water.

* Why should you add the washing water to the evaporating dish?

Dry the leftover zinc, and mass it.

* How much of the metal reacted with the hydrochloric
  acid?

Figure 6.6
Evaporating a solution in an evaporating dish heated directly over an alcohol burner.

The evaporating dish can be placed on a burner stand and heated using an alcohol burner, as shown in Figure 6.6. If the solution begins to spatter, move the flame gently back and forth.

Heat the material until it appears to be dry. Continue heating until the solid starts to melt and a tiny pool of liquid begins to form in the bottom of the evaporating dish. You can mass the dish and its contents as soon as they have cooled.

- What is the ratio of the mass of zinc reacted to the mass of zinc chloride formed?

- Compare your results with those of your classmates. Did an excess of either zinc or hydrochloric acid affect your results?

- If the zinc chloride were not completely dry when massed, how would this affect your ratio?

10 Suppose that in the synthesis of zinc chloride, you dissolved 5 g of zinc.
a) How much product would you get?
b) What would be the ratio of zinc to the product?
c) What would the ratio be if you dissolved 50 g of zinc?

11† In a certain package of seed corn, the number of red seeds was 36, and the number of yellow seeds was 24. In a second package, the number of red seeds was 51, and the number of yellow seeds was 34.
a) What is the ratio of the number of red seeds to the number of yellow seeds in each package?
b) What is the ratio of the number of red seeds to the total number of seeds in each package?

12 Suppose that there are 10 boys and 15 girls in a class.
a) What is the ratio of boys to girls in the class?
b) What is the ratio of boys to total number of students in the class?
c) What would be the ratio of boys to girls if the class were three times larger but the ratio of boys to total number of students was the same?

13† When various amounts of zinc react with hydrochloric acid, zinc chloride and hydrogen are produced. Which of the following ratios between the masses of various products and reacting substances are constant regardless of the amounts of zinc and acid mixed together?

(1) $\dfrac{\text{Zinc added}}{\text{Zinc chloride produced}}$

(4) $\dfrac{\text{Zinc used up}}{\text{Zinc chloride produced}}$

(2) $\dfrac{\text{Zinc used up}}{\text{Hydrochloric acid used up}}$

(5) $\dfrac{\text{Zinc added}}{\text{Hydrochloric acid added}}$

(3) $\dfrac{\text{Zinc used up}}{\text{Hydrogen produced}}$

(6) $\dfrac{\text{Zinc chloride produced}}{\text{Zinc used up}}$

(7) $\dfrac{\text{Hydrochloric acid used up}}{\text{Hydrogen produced}}$

6.5 THE LAW OF CONSTANT PROPORTIONS

In the last two sections, we studied the synthesis of two compounds: water from oxygen and hydrogen, and zinc chloride from zinc and hydrochloric acid. We found that hydrogen and oxygen combine only in the definite mass ratio of 0.13. It does not matter in what proportion we mix these gases. When they are ignited, we know that the hydrogen and the oxygen that react do so in a definite proportion to produce water. The zinc chloride that was produced in the last experiment was a result of the zinc combining with the chlorine in the hydrochloric acid. The ratio of the mass of zinc that reacted to the mass of zinc chloride was constant. It was independent of an excess either of hydrochloric acid or of zinc. This means that the ratio of zinc to the chlorine with which it combined also was constant.

We consider both water and zinc chloride to be compounds and not mixtures because each has characteristic properties quite different from those of the substances from which it is made. Do all substances combine in a constant proportion when they form compounds?

When you investigated the law of conservation of mass, there were two experiments in which compounds were formed. In one of these (Experiment 2.13), you heated copper and sulfur to make a new substance. Suppose we repeat the experiment, keeping the mass of copper constant and varying the mass of sulfur. Will we find that the mass of copper that reacts remains in a constant ratio to the mass of the product, independent of how much sulfur we use? This experiment has been done many times. As long as there is more than enough copper to react with all the sulfur, the ratio of the mass of the copper that undergoes reaction to the mass of the product remains fixed. But with an excess of sulfur, the ratio decreases. In this case, it appears at first that when copper and sulfur combine to form a compound, the ratio of the masses that react can vary.

The early chemists were in violent disagreement about the relative amount of substances that react to form compounds. On one side was a distinguished French chemist, Claude Louis Berthollet (1748–1822). He claimed, on the basis of experiments like the one with copper and sulfur, that a pair of substances can combine in any proportion to form a compound. On the other side was another distinguished French chemist, Joseph Louis Proust (1754–1826). He based his answer on evidence obtained from experiments that showed constant proportion, like the synthesis of water and of zinc chloride. Proust suggested a new law of nature, the law of constant proportions, which he stated thus in 1799: "We must recognize an invisible hand which holds the balance in the formation of compounds. A compound is a substance to which Nature assigns fixed ratios; it is, in short, a being which Nature never creates other than balance in hand." In plainer language, the law that Proust formulated can be stated as follows: When two substances combine to form a compound, they combine in a constant proportion. The ratio of the masses that react remains constant, no matter in what proportions they are mixed. If there is too much of one of the substances in the mixture, some of it will just not react.

When the law of constant proportions was formulated, the evidence in its favor was much weaker than the evidence you gathered for the law of the conservation of mass at the end of Chapter 2. In spite of much evidence that supported Berthollet's stand and that Proust could not explain, Proust was confident enough to claim constant proportions as a law of nature.

The explanation of results like those in the copper-sulfur reaction that seemed to support Berthollet's stand will be taken up later in the course.

---

14 If you make a solution of salt and water, over what range of values can you vary the mass ratio of salt to water at a given temperature?

15† a) Do you think that gasoline is a single compound? See Table 5.1 (p. 94).

b) Would you expect gasoline from different pumps to be the same?

6.6 EXPERIMENT   A REACTION WITH COPPER

Some substances react very fast. As you learned in section 6.3, when a test tube of hydrogen and oxygen is ignited, the reaction is very fast; indeed, it is explosive and ends in a fraction of a second. Solids usually do not react as fast as gases. In this experiment, you will investigate how the reaction of finely divided copper with oxygen in the air proceeds with time.

Mass a dry crucible and add about 1 g of copper dust. Now find, as accurately as possible, the total mass of the copper and the crucible.

Heat the copper, as shown in Figure 6.7, for 2 minutes. While heating, watch the copper carefully.

- Does a reaction take place?

When the crucible is cool, find the mass of the crucible and its contents.

- Did the crucible and its contents gain or lose mass?

- Is your answer to this question evidence that a reaction has taken place?

- What do you predict will happen if you continue to heat the crucible for an additional 10 to 15 minutes? Try it.

Break up the contents of the crucible with a scoopula and examine the pieces.

- Do you think that all the copper has reacted? If not, what fraction do you estimate did not react?

Do not discard the black solid in your crucible. Pour the pieces of solid into a test tube and save them for use in the next experiment.

6.7 EXPERIMENT   THE SEPARATION OF COPPER OXIDE FROM A MIXTURE OF COPPER OXIDE AND COPPER

If all the copper that you started with in the preceding experiment reacted with oxygen, then the black solid present at the end of the experiment would be the pure substance copper oxide. If, however, not all the copper reacted, then the black solid would be a mixture of copper and copper oxide. In order to determine whether the black solid is a mixture, we shall attempt to separate it.

A good way to separate a mixture like copper oxide and copper is to place the mixture in a solvent that will dissolve one of them but not the other. Copper will not easily dissolve in hydrochloric acid, as your teacher can show you. Copper oxide, on the other hand, is soluble in hydrochloric acid.

Figure 6.7
Powdered copper in a crucible supported by a triangle over an alcohol burner. The wires of the triangle are bent so that they can be hooked into holes in the pegboard for rigid support.

Place all the black solid you obtained in the previous experiment in a test tube. Add 5 cm³ of hydrochloric acid and stir gently with a glass stirring rod for 5 to 10 minutes. (**CAUTION:** Be careful not to get any hydrochloric acid on yourself or your books or clothes. If some acid spills on your hands, wash them thoroughly with water.) After letting the solid settle to the bottom, slowly pour off the liquid into another test tube. Now wash the remaining solid several times with water.

- What does the remaining solid look like?

- Was the black substance a mixture?

Do not discard the acid solution. You will need it for the first experiment in Chapter 7.

6.8 COMPLETE AND INCOMPLETE REACTIONS

Many reactions, like the reaction of copper with oxygen, are slow. It is difficult in these cases to tell when all of one of the reacting substances has been used up. Because the copper in your crucible changed to a black solid, you may have assumed that *all* the copper that was originally present in your crucible had reacted. This would have been an incorrect assumption, as the presence of copper in the black substance has shown.

Reactions like the reaction of copper with oxygen are called incomplete reactions because neither one of the reacting substances, copper or oxygen, is completely used up during the reaction. Other reactions, like the reaction of zinc with hydrochloric acid which you studied in section 6.4, are complete reactions. Zinc will keep on reacting with hydrochloric acid until either one of the two has been completely used up.

Part of the controversy that existed among early chemists about the validity of the law of constant proportions (section 6.5) could have been avoided if they had better analyzed what actually happened during their experiments. Some of their disagreements occurred because they did not understand the difference between complete and incomplete reactions. Specifically, they often mistook the masses they mixed for the masses that reacted. As your own experience shows, this mistake is easy to make.

For Home, Desk, and Lab

16 a) How would you have changed the procedure you followed in Experiment 6.1 if you had wanted to measure the density of the gas?
b) Would you have had to decompose all the sodium chlorate in order to determine the density of the gas?

17 Ten grams of sodium chlorate was strongly heated. After the heating it was found that 5 cm^3 of water at 100°C was required to dissolve completely a 2-g sample of the residue.
a) What was the solubility of the residue in grams per 100 cm^3 of water at 100°C?
b) Was any sodium chlorate left in the residue?

18 Suppose that the apparatus used in Experiment 6.2 on the decomposition of water contained 100 cm^3 of water. Using this apparatus, a student collected 57 cm^3 of hydrogen and 28 cm^3 of oxygen. What fraction of the total volume of water was decomposed?

19 About a gram of salt is placed in a test tube half full of water and shaken; about a gram of citric acid is placed in a test tube filled with alcohol and shaken; some magnesium carbonate is dropped into half a test tube of dilute sulfuric acid; hydrochloric acid is poured into a dish containing magnesium. In each case, the solid disappears, and we say that it "dissolved." However, it is evident that two different kinds of dissolving have occurred. Divide the experiments into two classes. What did you observe that led you to divide them this way? What do you think you will observe in each case if you evaporate the solution to dryness?

20 A mass of 5.00 g of oxygen combines with 37.2 g of uranium to form uranium oxide.
a) How many grams of the oxide are formed?
b) What is the ratio of uranium to oxygen in this compound?
c) How much oxygen is needed to oxidize completely 100 g of uranium?

21 Discuss the process of boiling an egg in terms of complete and incomplete reactions. What may affect the time required for a complete reaction?

22 What evidence do you have for the following statements?
a) Zinc chloride is a pure substance and not a mixture.
b) Sodium chlorate is a pure substance and not a mixture of sodium chloride and oxygen.
c) Water is a pure substance.

23 A student heated a crucible containing 2.15 g of powdered copper until the mass of the contents of the crucible became 2.42 g. The black solid in the crucible was placed in hydrochloric acid, and 1.08 g of copper remained undissolved in the acid. What is the reacting ratio by mass of copper with oxygen?

24 Hydrochloric acid is a solution of the compound hydrogen chloride in water. Suppose there were two bottles containing hydrochloric acid in your lab. How would you determine whether the concentration of hydrogen chloride in each bottle is the same?

Themes for Short Essays

1 "Seeing is believing" is a common saying. But does "not seeing" imply "not believing"? Neither hydrogen nor oxygen is visible in Figure 6.4 or in the laboratory. Is there, perhaps, a form of indirect seeing? Express your thoughts on this subject.

2 Express the essence of Section 6.5 as a debate between Bertholet and Proust.

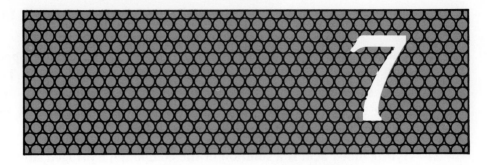

Elements

7.1 EXPERIMENT ZINC AND COPPER

When you heated a sample of finely divided copper in Experiment 6.6: A Reaction with Copper, its mass increased. This indicated that something was being added to the copper. A new substance, copper oxide, was formed. In Experiment 6.7, you dissolved the copper oxide in hydrochloric acid, and from the black powder you produced a blue-green solution.

What happened to the copper in all these reactions? Did it disappear forever, or is it still in the solution in some form? Putting a piece of zinc in the solution will provide you with an answer. **CAUTION:** As you know from the synthesis of zinc chloride, zinc in hydrochloric acid will generate heat. Therefore, for safety reasons, it is advisable to put the test tube containing the solution in a beaker half filled with water, as you did in Experiment 6.4.

Put a piece of zinc in the solution you saved from Experiment 6.7, and observe the reaction. While the reaction is going on, break up the solid from time to time with a stirring rod.

After the zinc has finished reacting, pour off the solution from the remaining solid and wash the solid several times with water to remove the acid from it. The washed solid should be removed from the test tube and dried quickly by pressing it between two layers of paper towel.

Press a scoopula firmly against the paper towel and move it across the dry solid.

- Can you identify the solid?

1† What would happen if you heated the solid that you recovered in this experiment?

2 How do you expect the total mass of solid recovered in Experiments 6.7 and 7.1 to compare with the initial mass of copper you heated in Experiment 6.6?

7.2 ELEMENTS

Heating copper in air is not the only way to produce a reaction with copper. There are many other reactions, and they all have one feature in common: The product of the reaction always has a larger mass than the mass of copper. Neither heating nor electrolysis will make something out of copper that has a smaller mass than did the copper with which we started.

Contrast this behavior of copper with that of sodium chlorate (Experiment 6.1). When you heat sodium chlorate, oxygen is given off, and the resulting sodium chloride has a smaller mass. We reason, therefore, that sodium chloride is a simpler substance than sodium chlorate.

In Experiment 6.2, we electrolyzed water, causing it to decompose into hydrogen and oxygen. In the same way, molten sodium chloride can be decomposed by electrolysis into chlorine and sodium. The mass of either the chlorine alone or the sodium alone is less than the mass of the sodium chloride from which they were produced. Thus, sodium and chlorine are simpler substances than sodium chloride. However, just as with copper, none of the methods that can be used to break up other substances work for either sodium or chlorine. Pure substances that do not break up by heating, electrolysis, reacting with acids, or similar methods are called "elements."

It is not necessary, of course, to try to break up the many thousands of pure substances we know in order to find out which of them are elements. In many cases, we know substances are compounds simply because they can be made by combining other substances. For example, we can "burn" sodium in an atmosphere of chlorine gas. The resulting white solid has the characteristic properties of table salt. Thus, table salt is not an element; it is the compound sodium chloride.

Early chemists using this reasoning were able to select as possible elements a relatively small number of substances from the list of pure substances they knew. One such list, proposed by the French chemist Lavoisier in 1789 was accompanied by the following explanation: "Since we have not hitherto discovered the means of separating them, they act with regard to us as simple substances, and we ought never to suppose them compounded until experiment and observation have proved them to be so."

Lavoisier's list of elements included several well known substances which are also found on today's list of elements; among them are iron, copper, silver, gold, hydrogen, oxygen, and carbon. From a historical point of view, two substances are of special interest. One was on Lavoisier's list and one was not.

The first substance is lime, which can be produced by strongly heating common limestone. Lime was known to the Romans as early as 200 B.C. Many attempts were made over the years to decompose lime: The substance was heated in air, heated in a vacuum, and heated with carbon. Every attempt failed, and most people agreed that lime must be an element. There were a few doubters, who thought that lime was probably a compound of a metal with oxygen. They thought that lime could not be decomposed simply because the usual agent, carbon, which worked with copper oxide and other oxides, was somehow not "powerful" enough to separate the oxygen from the metal.

As so often happens, a new discovery had to wait for a new experimental method. In this case, the electric battery, invented by Alessandro Volta in 1800, was the necessary tool. In 1807, the English chemist Humphry Davy used an electric battery to try to decompose metal oxides. He had already used a battery to decompose molten potash and molten soda to obtain the new elements potassium and sodium. A similar procedure failed to work with lime because lime could not be melted. After much experimentation, however, Davy finally succeeded. He was able, by carefully electrolyzing moist lime, to produce tiny amounts of a new element he called "calcium."

Missing from Lavoisier's list was a very reactive gas, slightly green in color. It was discovered in 1774 as a by-product of some experiments with muriatic acid. (Muriatic acid we now call "hydrochloric acid.") Various people experimented with the new gas and found it similar in many ways to the gases from other strong acids. Acids were considered in those days to be substances that were strongly corrosive and had a sour taste. Since oxygen was believed at that time to be the active ingredient in all acids, this new substance was named "oxymuriatic acid gas."

This name stuck for more than thirty years, mainly because it had been suggested by some very important and respected chemists. Several people tried, unsuccessfully, to decompose the gas. They always blamed their failures on poor methods and poor tools. In 1810, Humphry Davy, after working with his usual patience and brilliance for a full two years, finally announced the results of his long series of experiments. These experiments, in his own words, "... incline me to believe that the body improperly called oxymuriatic acid gas has not as yet been decompounded; but that it is a peculiar substance, elementary as far as our knowledge extends, and similar in many of its properties to oxygen gas. . . ." In order that people would no longer be misled into thinking it a compound, he suggested a new name, "based upon one of its obvious and characteristic properties—its color," and called it "chlorine." Davy's conclusion has stood the tests both of time and new techniques, and chlorine is included in the present-day list of elements.

---

3   While on a class field trip, a student found a shiny rock that appeared to be a metal. When she returned to the classroom, she heated the rock for a while and found that it lost mass. Further heating did not affect the mass. Could this rock be an element? Explain your answer.

4   How do you know that water, zinc chloride, and sodium chlorate are not elements?

5   Hydrogen chloride—a gaseous pure substance—can be decomposed into two different gases, each of which acts like a pure substance. On the basis of this evidence alone:
    a)   Can hydrogen chloride be an element?
    b)   Can either of the other two gases be an element?
    c)   Can you be sure that any of the pure substances mentioned is an element?

7.3 ELEMENTS NEAR THE SURFACE OF THE EARTH

Today's list of elements contains 106 entries. Only 50 elements are commonly used; they are listed in Table 7.1. The elements on the left side of the table are listed in decreasing order of abundance near the surface of the earth. The elements on the right side of the table are listed alphabetically; their abundance is less than that of argon and is not listed.

Table 7.1 Elements Found Near the Surface of the Earth

Name	Symbol	Abundance (in % by mass)	Name	Symbol
Oxygen	O	65.5	Arsenic	As
Silicon	Si	13.7	Boron	B
Hydrogen	H	5.4	Bromine	Br
Aluminum	Al	4.2	Cadmium	Cd
Iron	Fe	3.1	Cesium	Cs
Calcium	Ca	2.4	Cobalt	Co
Sodium	Na	1.7	Germanium	Ge
Magnesium	Mg	1.5	Gold	Au
Chlorine	Cl	0.95	Helium	He
Potassium	K	0.94	Iodine	I
Titanium	Ti	0.32	Krypton	Kr
Nitrogen	N	0.14	Lead	Pb
Sulfur	S	0.061	Lithium	Li
Phosphorus	P	0.060	Mercury	Hg
Manganese	Mn	0.053	Neon	Ne
Fluorine	F	0.028	Osmium	Os
Barium	Ba	0.020	Platinum	Pt
Strontium	Sr	0.019	Polonium	Po
Carbon	C	0.010	Radium	Ra
Vanadium	V	0.0067	Radon	Rn
Chromium	Cr	0.0060	Silver	Ag
Nickel	Ni	0.0050	Tin	Sn
Zinc	Zn	0.0039	Tungsten	W
Copper	Cu	0.0034	Uranium	U
Argon	Ar	0.0023	Xenon	Xe

The part of the earth for which abundance was calculated includes the atmosphere, the oceans, and the ground to a depth of one kilometer below the surface (including that below the oceans).

The data used in the calculations are based on the analysis of thousands of samples of soil, sea water, and air collected at many locations.

Note how few elements account for most of the mass around us. The first five elements (oxygen to iron) in the left column of Table 7.1 account for almost 92% of the total mass of the elements found near the surface of the earth. Oxygen, the most abundant element, occurs in many compounds found in the ground. Ordinary sand contains mostly silicon dioxide, a compound of oxygen and silicon. Silicon dioxide is also the main ingredient of glass. Hydrogen, the third element in Table 7.1, is found primarily in the oceans. The 56 elements not listed in Table 7.1 together account for less than 0.001% of the mass near the earth's surface.

6 How many elements collectively compose 99% of the mass of the earth *accessible* to people?

7 Data for the elemental composition of living matter were not used to calculate the abundance of the elements listed in Table 7.1. Even so, the data in Table 7.1 are correct. How do you think that this can be so?

8 The total mass of the one-kilometer layer of ground, the oceans, and the atmosphere is 2.8×10^{21} kg. What is the mass of (a) iron, (b) sulfur, and (c) copper near the surface of the earth?

7.4 THE PRODUCTION OF IRON AND ALUMINUM

Our industrial civilization requires large quantities of metallic elements. Among the most important ones are iron and aluminum. Materials found in the ground from which metals can be profitably extracted are called "ores." Ores of a given element may include a number of different compounds of that element. The most important ores of iron and aluminum are their oxides. Ores are usually found mixed with unwanted substances from which they have to be separated before the metal can be extracted.

It has been known for over three thousand years that if iron ore is mixed with coal or charcoal and heated strongly, iron is produced. In recent times, the same process has been carried out in huge blast furnaces.

Figure 7.1
A general view of a modern blast furnace close to 100 m high. The passageway on the right contains the conveyer belt that brings the ore, coke, and limestone to the top of the furnace. (*Bethlehem Steel Corporation*)

Figure 7.1 provides an overall view of a modern blast furnace. The covered passage on the right contains the conveyor, which carries a mixture of iron ore, coke (a form of carbon), and crushed limestone to the top of the furnace. Air preheated in the four stoves on the left is forced into the lower part of the furnace.

Fierce burning of the coke raises the temperature to over 1650°C. Carbon monoxide is formed, which, together with the coke, removes the oxygen from the iron. The iron melts and settles to the bottom of the furnace.

The limestone combines with the impurities in the ore to form slag, which melts and floats on top of the liquid iron. The slag prevents the iron from recombining with the oxygen in the incoming air. The molten iron and slag are drawn off from time to time.

The gases from the top of the furnace contain carbon monoxide. These gases are piped to the stoves, and the carbon monoxide is burned there to preheat the air going into the furnace. Figure 7.2 is a schematic drawing of the blast furnace and one of the stoves. Figure 7.3 shows molten iron flowing through clay-lined channels into a container before being further processed into steel.

Aluminum, like iron, is a widely used element. The most important ore of aluminum, bauxite, is about 50 percent aluminum oxide. Pure aluminum oxide is obtained by dissolving the ore in a

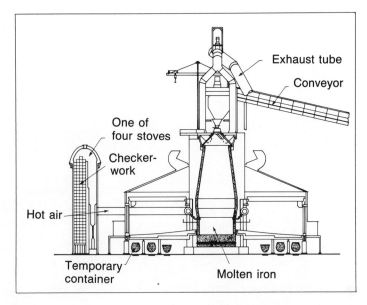

Figure 7.2

A schematic drawing of the blast furnace and stove. Gases from the blast furnace are mixed with air and burned in the right side of the stove. The hot gases then go through a checkerwork of fire bricks, making the bricks red hot. After about half an hour, the burning is stopped and fresh air is pushed through the checkerwork in the opposite direction. The air heats up and is forced into the blast furnace.

Figure 7.3

Molten iron flowing from the furnace. Because of its high temperature it glows brightly. The big ring near the top of the photograph contains the pipes for the hot air (as shown schematically in Figure 7.2). (*Bethlehem Steel Corporation*)

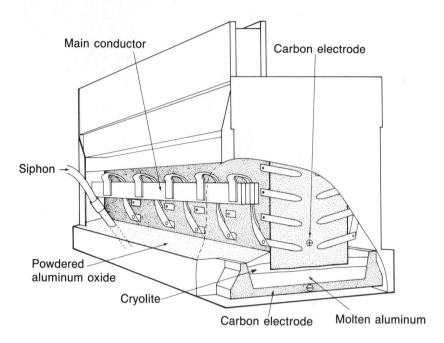

Figure 7.4
A schematic drawing of an aluminum-producing cell.

suitable solvent, filtering out the unwanted solids, and letting the aluminum oxide crystallize.

Unlike iron, aluminum cannot be freed from its oxide in a blast furnace. It was only about 100 years ago that a way was discovered to separate aluminum from oxygen by electrolysis. Aluminum oxide is first dissolved in molten cryolite (a compound of sodium, aluminum, and fluorine) at a temperature of around 1000°C. The electrolysis takes place in a large rectangular metal container called a cell. A schematic drawing of a cell is shown in Figure 7.4.

The cell is lined with carbon, which serves as the negative electrode ($-$). A large carbon block at the center forms the positive electrode ($+$). The electric current reaches the block through a set of pins. The cryolite is heated and kept molten by the passage of electricity through it. Liquid aluminum gathers at the bottom of the cell and is siphoned off. The oxygen from the aluminum oxide combines with the carbon in the block. The resulting gases are vented off, and the carbon block is slowly eaten away. The block is pushed down and from time to time a new set of pins is connected to the

(a)

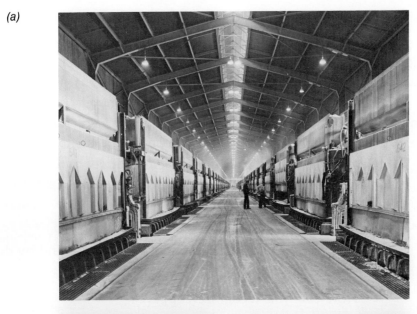

(b)

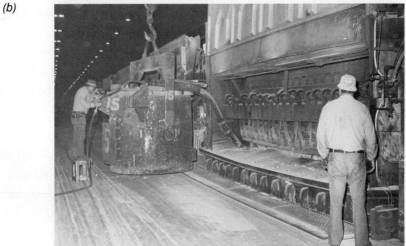

Figure 7.5
(a) Inside view of a large aluminum plant. (b) The cover of a cell is raised to show the carbon block and the connection to the main conductor. The siphon is on the left. (*Courtesy of Reynolds Aluminum, Jan Fardel*)

main conductor. After a while the block is replaced. Figure 7.5(a) shows a long row of cells. In 7.5(b), the nearest cell has its cover removed to show the glowing contents of the cell and carbon block.

The density of aluminum is only about one-third that of iron. Therefore, aluminum is used where low mass is desirable, as in airplane bodies.

7.5 EXPERIMENT FLAME TESTS OF SOME ELEMENTS

As you have seen, some compounds are hard to break up into their elements. However, by holding small samples in a flame, even such compounds can be made to reveal the elements that they contain.

Place small quantities of different compounds, each of which contains sodium, on tiny loops of nichrome wire and hold them in a flame. Record the color you see for each of the compounds.

Next, try the same experiment using copper and compounds that contain copper, and then using strontium. Try a sample of a compound containing lithium and then a sample containing calcium.

- How can you recognize sodium in a compound by doing such a flame test?

- How can you recognize copper?

- Can you distinguish among strontium, calcium, and lithium compounds by a flame test?

---

9   When you hold a small amount of sodium chloride in a flame, you observe that the flame is strongly colored yellow. What could you do to be sure that the color is due to the sodium and not to chlorine?

10† If you spill a few drops of soup or milk on a pale-blue gas flame when cooking, the flame changes to a mixture of colors, with yellow being the most intense color. How do you explain this fact?

7.6 EXPERIMENT SPECTRA OF SOME ELEMENTS

In the preceding experiment, you found that some elements are easy to distinguish by the colors their compounds give when heated in a flame. Many elements are not so easily identified. For such elements, we need a way to separate the mixed colors so that we can detect slight differences in color that the eye cannot normally detect. The first step is to spread out the various colors in the light in much the same way they are in a rainbow. This spread of colors is called a "spectrum" (plural: spectra).

You can produce a spectrum using a simple grating spectroscope. This device consists of a tube with a slit on one end and a piece of a transparent plastic disk on the other. The disk has many parallel lines impressed on it.

Hold the end with the plastic grating next to your eye and look at several light sources provided by your teacher. (When the light source is a thin tube, you may find it more convenient to look at the light with the slit end removed.)

- What is the major difference between the spectrum of an ordinary light bulb and the spectrum of any of the gas tubes?

- What are the differences between the spectra of the different gas tubes?

7.7 SPECTRAL ANALYSIS

We mentioned compounds of calcium, lithium, and strontium without specifying which compounds we were talking about. This may have given you the impression that only the spectrum of one of the elements in a compound can be observed. It is true that the flame of your alcohol burner is hot enough to produce the spectra of sodium, lithium, calcium, copper, and a few other elements, but that it is not hot enough to produce the other spectra of elements, such as oxygen and chlorine. However, if we heat a sample of a compound to a sufficiently high temperature (for example, by putting it in an electric arc), the spectra of all the elements in the compound will be observed. Under such conditions, the resulting spectrum is no longer simple. It will most likely contain complicated patterns of many closely spaced lines. Yet each element gives out its own spectrum, which is different from that of any other. It takes accurate measurements of the positions of spectral lines to identify an element. Once this has been done, however, the presence of that element has been definitely established.

With a good instrument, the sodium spectrum looks like Figure 7.6 (page 147). This shows that the yellow of the sodium flame is not just any yellow. It is a very specific color indeed, which has its own special place in the spectrum. It is a yellow made by no other element. The presence of this particular pair of lines always means that sodium is present in the light source. Even if the yellow color is hidden from the unaided eye by many other colors, the spectroscope will show the presence of sodium.

Figure 7.7 (page 147) illustrates spectra obtained from compounds of calcium, lithium, and strontium. Although all these elements give flame tests of nearly the same color, we see that each gives its own set of characteristic spectral lines when viewed through a spectroscope. The spectroscope thus enables us to distinguish one element from another.

Spectral analysis, or spectroscopy, can be done on tiny quantities of matter, such as a very small sample of a rare mineral or of a biological material. Spectroscopy can even be used to determine the presence of different elements in distant objects like our sun and other stars.

Analysis of sunlight was one of the very early uses of the spectroscope in the study of unknown matter. Most of the spectral lines observed in sunlight could also be produced with known materials in the laboratory. However, during a solar eclipse in 1868, a new set of spectral lines was found in the spectrum of the light coming from the edge of the sun. This set of lines had never been seen before and could not be produced with any element known at the time. The lines were therefore thought to be from a new element, which was given the name "helium," after the Greek word for sun. Eventually, the element was also detected on earth through the use of a spectroscope.

During the first few years of spectroscopy, five new elements were discovered that are present on earth in such small concentrations that they were previously unknown. For example, in analyzing the spectrum of minerals found in the water of a certain spring in Germany, two lines of unknown origin were found in the blue region of the spectrum. This bit of evidence was enough to challenge Robert Bunsen, the German chemist, to search for a new element in the water. In order to isolate some of the pure element, which he named "cesium," it was necessary to evaporate 40,000 kg of spring water! In more recent times, spectral analysis has been one of the tools found helpful in identifying some of the new elements produced by nuclear reactions.

Time after time, this interplay between chemical analysis and spectral analysis has caused complex substances to yield the secret of their composition. Invariably, the results given by these two different methods agree completely.

This is roughly how the spectra would appear if they were photographed on color film.

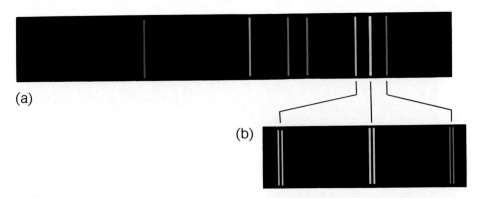

(a)

(b)

Figure 7.6
(a) The spectrum of sodium. The line in the yellow is extremely intense. It has been photographed through an absorbing filter, because otherwise it could not be photographed well at the same time as the other lines. The close pair of almost invisible violet lines arises from a potassium impurity. (b) A part of the sodium spectrum has been photographed with a spectroscope that spreads out the light more, enabling us to see more detail. It shows that the yellow sodium line is really made up of two lines very close together.

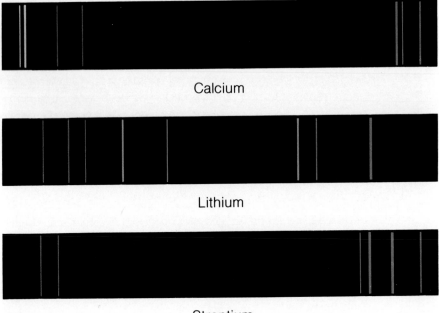

Calcium

Lithium

Strontium

Figure 7.7
The brightest lines in the spectra of calcium, lithium, and strontium.

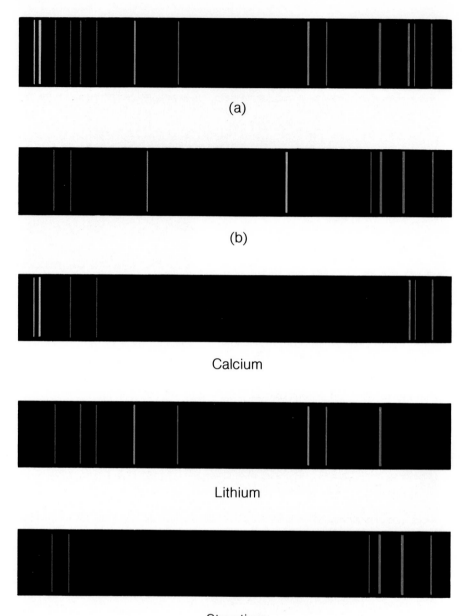

(a)

(b)

Calcium

Lithium

Strontium

Figure A
For Problem 11

11 Figure A (page 148) shows some spectra observed with the same spectroscope that was used to obtain the spectra illustrated in Figure 7.7. What elements can you identify in (*a*)? In (*b*)?

12 Suppose that you are given a sample of a substance. How would you try to find out if the substance is an element, a compound, or a mixture?

7.8 RADIOACTIVE ELEMENTS

We have now reached a high point in our study of matter. Through simple experiments, you have been able to trace the main steps that led to a recognition of how the material world is put together. The accomplishments of the past few centuries are really impressive: The millions of mixtures around us are now known to be made up of tens of thousands of compounds, which in turn are composed of only about a hundred elements. Compounds have characteristic properties that are different from those of the elements from which they are made. Yet the elements never really disappear. Their presence and their identity are revealed by their spectra, and they can always be extracted from their compounds. Elements seem to be permanent.

In science, however, it often happens that a new phenomenon is observed just when we think our understanding of a subject is complete. We find that our picture of the situation is incomplete; some important details need to be added.

In the case of elements, it was found that some substances that qualified as elements were in fact *not* permanent, but changed on their own into other elements. The ground-breaking experiment leading to this discovery was made by the French physicist Henri Becquerel in 1896. We shall now describe a modern version of his experiment.* Six plastic boxes containing samples of different materials were placed on a photographic film. The film was wrapped in black paper to shield it from the light. After three days, the film was

---

*The details of this experiment are shown in the *Introductory Physical Science* film loop titled "Radioactive Substances I."

Figure 7.8
Six different substances in small plastic boxes are placed on a photographic film enclosed in black paper. The boxes are left in position for three days before the film is developed.

Figure 7.9
The film in Figure 7.8 after being developed. The three white squares appear where the boxes A, C, and E in Figure 7.8 were placed.

developed. Figure 7.8 shows where the boxes were placed. Figure 7.9 shows three white squares on the developed film where boxes A, C, and E were placed. Apparently, the material in these boxes gave off something that was able to get through the black paper and affect the film in the way that light does.

The elements contained in the boxes (all in compounds, except that in box F) are listed in Table 7.2. Boxes A and B had two elements in common: sulfur and oxygen. However, box A, not box B, affected the film. This suggests that uranium was the element that emitted or radiated something. This conclusion is supported by the fact that box C, which also contained uranium, left a mark on the photographic film.

Similarly, a comparison of the contents of boxes D and E suggests that the thorium in box E is the cause of the mark on the film.

Table 7.2

Box	Elements
A	Uranium, sulfur, oxygen
B	Sodium, sulfur, oxygen
C	Uranium, nitrogen, oxygen
D	Sodium, nitrogen, oxygen
E	Thorium, nitrogen, oxygen
F	Sulfur

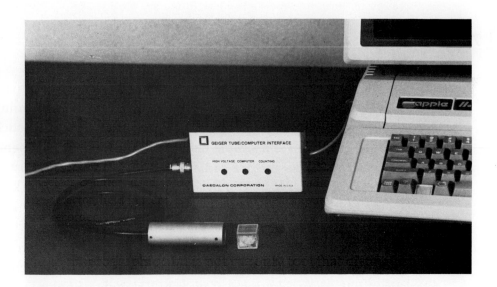

Figure 7.10
A Geiger counter, used to detect radiation from radioactive sources. The detector, held in front, is connected to the computer, which serves as a recorder.

Photographic film is not the only tool that distinguishes boxes A, C, and E from the others. If we place any one of these boxes near an instrument called a Geiger counter (Figure 7.10), the counter will count or produce clicks that can be counted. Boxes B, D, and F do not affect the counter at all.

There are other elements listed in Table 7.1 that radiate something that affects a photographic film and a Geiger counter. These elements are called "radioactive" elements.

13† Elements X, Y, and Z form compounds XY, XZ, and YZ. Compounds XY and YZ are radioactive, but XZ is not. Which element is radioactive?

14 A piece of magnesium placed in hydrochloric acid causes hydrogen to be released. Evaporation of the resulting solution leaves behind a white solid. A similar reaction occurs when a piece of uranium is placed in hydrochloric acid. Would you expect this white solid to be radioactive?

7.9 RADIOACTIVE DECOMPOSITION

What happens to a radioactive element when it radiates? This is a hard question to answer. Some elements, such as uranium, radiate so weakly that it is extremely difficult to discover what is happening to them. Other radioactive elements, such as polonium, emit such intense radiation that it is a simple task to determine what happens. However, because of its intense radiation, even a milligram (10^{-3} g) of polonium is a health hazard unless special precautions are taken. Despite the difficulties, both weakly and strongly radiating elements have been studied.

In the case of polonium, spectral analysis reveals the secret. A freshly prepared sample of polonium has a spectrum that is characteristic of polonium. However, if we seal a sample of polonium in an evacuated glass tube and examine its spectrum a few weeks later, the spectrum will be quite different. In addition to the lines of polonium, the lines of helium and lead—two elements that were not present before—can be detected. If we check the spectrum after an additional month or two, we find that the polonium lines get weaker, and the lead and helium lines get stronger.

Apparently, the radiation from polonium is connected with the change of polonium into lead and helium. Spectral analysis shows that other radioactive elements also change into different elements. In many cases, helium is one of the elements that is produced. We refer to this process as "radioactive decomposition" or "radioactive decay."

Is radioactive decomposition different from the decomposition of water or other compounds? You remember that the products of the decomposition of water could be recombined to form the original compound. Lime, which Lavoisier thought to be an element, was finally decomposed into calcium and oxygen by electrolysis, but the calcium and oxygen easily recombine. It has been found possible to recombine all the elements that have been obtained from compounds. However, we have not been able to recombine the products of radioactive decomposition by using the methods we have already described to recombine elements into compounds.

What happens to a radioactive element when it is heated? Does heat change the rate at which it emits radiation? In many of the experiments you have done and read about in this course, temperature has had an important effect on what happened and how fast it happened. Wood decomposed when you heated it in a closed tube; the hotter the wood became, the faster it decomposed. Hydrogen does not burn by itself in air, but when it is heated with the flame of a burning match, it catches fire very easily—sometimes explosively.

To find out whether temperature has any effect on the intensity of radiation from radioactive substances, samples of these substances have been heated to very high temperatures, and they have been cooled to very low temperatures in liquid air. But it was found that temperature changes do not affect the radiation from a radioactive substance.

To sum up, the radioactive elements have all the properties of elements that you have studied in the preceding chapters. They form compounds with constant composition and have their characteristic densities, melting and boiling points, and spectra. They cannot be decomposed by ordinary heat, electricity, reaction with acids, and the like. They differ from nonradioactive elements in that they affect a photographic film and decompose into other elements. The rate at which they decompose cannot be changed by any of the means that affect the rate at which compounds decompose. That is why we call these substances elements; but to set them apart, we call them radioactive elements.

15† A single sample of uranium nitrate was left on a piece of photographic film for a week. During the week, the sample was moved twice to new spots on the film. When the film was developed, the three "exposed" areas were found to vary in intensity.
a) What can you conclude about the temperature variation during the week?
b) What can you conclude about the length of time the sample was in each position?

16 What are the two most important differences between the following two reactions?
a) Water → hydrogen + oxygen
b) Polonium → lead + helium

17 A radioactive sample at 20°C is placed near a device that counts the radiation coming from the sample. The counter records 1.0×10^2 counts/minute. The temperature of the sample is then raised to 100°C. What does the counter then record?

7.10   A CLOSER LOOK AT RADIOACTIVITY

We have seen evidence that some elements come from other elements. Now let us try to get a closer look at how this happens.

A simple device called a cloud chamber (Figure 7.11) will provide some useful clues. Figure 7.12 shows a photograph of a cloud chamber that contains a sample of polonium. You can see individual tracks originating from the sample. The tracks are formed instantaneously—as far as one can tell by just looking. Nevertheless, it seems reasonable that they are formed by very fast particles flying off from the radioactive source. Watching a cloud chamber in operation (either directly or on film), you will notice that the tracks shoot off irregularly. Even after watching the chamber for a long time you will not be able to tell when the next track will be made and in which direction it will go. Only the average number of tracks produced in a long time interval can be predicted from past observations.

Such direct observations, though very instructive, are tedious. The Geiger counter connected to a computer allows us not only to gather information easily but also to display it immediately in the form of a histogram.

Figure 7.11

A simple cloud chamber. The chamber itself is a cylindrical plastic box resting on a block of dry ice. A dark felt band, soaked in methanol, encircles the inside of the top of the chamber. A tiny radioactive source is placed on the end of the needle projecting into the chamber. The needle is supported by a cork stopper inserted into a hole in the wall of the cylindrical box. The bottom of the chamber is painted black so that the white fog tracks will be easily seen when viewed from above and illuminated from the side.

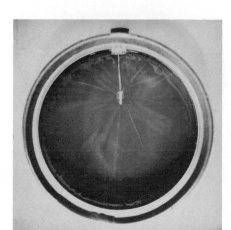

Figure 7.12

Fog tracks produced in a cloud chamber by the radiation from a radioactive source placed on the end of a needle. The preparation of a cloud chamber and the formation of tracks are shown in the *IPS* film loop "Radioactive Substances II."

Source C (Table 7.2) was placed in front of the counter shown in Figure 7.10. The computer recorded the number of counts in 100 equal time intervals. A histogram of the results is shown in Figure 7.13(*a*). Like the tracks produced in the cloud chamber, the counts are irregular. In some time intervals there were only 23–25 counts, in others there were up to 46 counts. In another run of 100 equal time intervals, the histogram looks quite different (Figure 7.13(*b*)). Only the average number of counts is about the same.

This kind of behavior is characteristic of events that happen by chance. For example, suppose you throw 10 dice many times. You would expect to find on the average $\frac{10}{6}$ dice showing a six on the upper face in each throw. In each throw of 10 dice you are likely

(a)

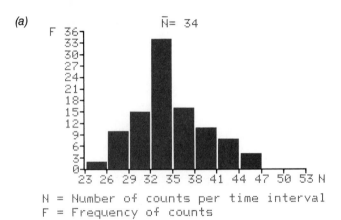

N = Number of counts per time interval
F = Frequency of counts

(b)

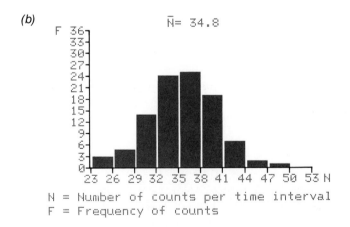

N = Number of counts per time interval
F = Frequency of counts

Figure 7.13
Two runs of 100 equal time intervals each. The average number of counts per interval ($\bar{N}$) is practically the same in both runs. But the detailed distributions are quite different, as shown in the two computer printouts.

to find one or two sixes. However in some cases you will find three or more sixes, or none at all.

The experiments with cloud chambers and Geiger counters suggest that radioactive decompositions take place in "discrete," or countable, steps. Combining this observation with the fact that elements are produced during radioactive decomposition leads to a far-reaching conclusion: Elements are made up of discrete units, or some sort of tiny particles, called "atoms."

Historically, the idea that elements are made up of atoms preceded the discovery of radioactivity. We have chosen to introduce this idea by discussing radioactivity because radioactivity enables us to count individual events in which new atoms are made (and old ones disappear).

18† In Figure 7.13(a), how many readings occurred in which there were 32, 33, or 34 counts per time interval?

19 Can you tell whether the tracks in Figure 7.12 are slanting upward, are slanting downward, or are horizontal?

20 Summarize the similarities between radioactive decay as observed with a cloud chamber and with a Geiger counter.

For Home, Desk, and Lab

21 When magnesium is put into hydrochloric acid, the metal reacts, a gas bubbles off, and a white solid is left behind after evaporation.
a) On the basis of this information alone, can you be sure which of the pure substances mentioned are compounds and which are elements?
b) We then find that the gas reacts just like hydrogen gas; it has the same characteristic properties. Also we find that hydrochloric acid can be decomposed into hydrogen and chlorine. Can the remaining solid be an element?

c)   From the table of elements (Table 7.1, page 138), which of the substances mentioned above are elements and which are compounds?

22   Use your grating spectroscope to examine the spectra of several light sources outside of your school (except the sun, which is too bright and will damage your eyes!). How do they compare with the light sources you examined in Experiment 7.6? Make a record of your observations and bring it to class.

23   a)   If you heat a piece of blue vitriol (a blue solid), it loses mass and changes to a white powder. Which of the two substances might be an element?
b)   If you dissolve the white powder in water and place an iron nail (iron is an element) in the solution, the nail will become coated with a thin layer of copper. What do you now conclude about the two substances in part (a)? Is either of them an element?

24   A plant absorbs various substances through its roots. Different elements of these substances concentrate in different parts of the plant. Suppose one of these elements is radioactive. How would you determine in what parts of the plant it concentrates?

25   In the film loop "Radioactive Substances I," the Geiger counter counted much faster when box A was placed next to it than when box E was. Is this what you would have expected on the basis of the brightness of the white patches in Figure 7.9? Why or why not?

26   You saw in the film loop "Radioactive Substances I" that a Geiger counter counts something even if it is not placed near a radioactive source. Taking this fact into account, how would you measure the number of clicks per hour caused by a radioactive source?

27   The film loop "Radioactive Substances II" shows tracks being produced in a cloud chamber. From what you see in the loop, can you be sure that the tracks start at the source rather than end there? What does this tell you about the speed of the particles that leave the tracks?

28   Figure B shows a histogram of another run of 100 equal time intervals, made with the same apparatus as for those in Figure 7.13. Estimate the average number ($\bar{N}$) of counts per time interval for this run. How does this $\bar{N}$ compare with those of Figure 7.13?

Figure B

For problem 28

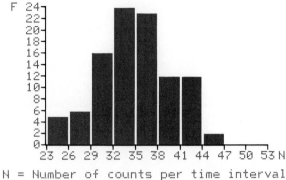

N = Number of counts per time interval
F = Frequency of counts

Themes for Short Essays

1   A local newspaper printed a letter from a person who wrote, "Aluminum is plentiful; and if I buy an aluminum can, I can do what I please with it." Write a letter to the editor in reply to this person.

2   Write two encyclopedia entries for the word "element," one that might have appeared before Becquerel's discovery and one thirty years after it.

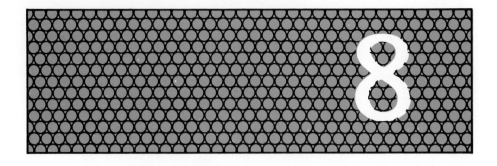

The Atomic Model of Matter

8.1 A MODEL

When you look at a steel bar, pour water into a cup, or listen to the hiss of air leaking from a tire, you feel quite sure that matter is continuous. It does not look or act as though it is made of individual particles. But the black dots on the photographic film, the individual tracks in the cloud chamber, and the clearly countable clicks of the Geiger counter suggest a different picture—a picture in which matter is grainy or discrete.

To help illustrate what we mean by "grainy or discrete" in describing radioactivity, we can visualize a spray can spraying droplets of paint. Such a picture must not be taken as an exact representation. Of course we know that a piece of polonium does not look like a spray can, and we do not believe for a moment that the little particles that produce tracks in the cloud chamber are made of paint. We use a specific example or analogy as an illustration for a more abstract idea. The droplets of paint really stand for some kind of small particles, each of which can make a Geiger counter click or leave a track in the cloud chamber. If there are more particles, more tracks will be left; but the individual tracks are not affected by the number of particles. This abstract description of the radioactive process in terms of particles is an example of a "model," or a theory. This particle model clearly accounts for the increase in the blackening of a photographic plate with increasing exposure time.

For a model, such as the particle model of matter, to be really useful, it has to offer us more than merely a convenient way of summarizing and accounting for facts we already know. A model must also enable us to make predictions. Here is an example of a very simple model and a prediction we can make from it: Suppose someone hands you a sealed tin can. You shake it and hear and feel something slosh around inside. From this simple experiment of shaking the can, you form a mental picture—a model—of what is inside. You conclude that the can contains a liquid. You have no idea what color the liquid is or what it tastes or smells like, but you feel sure that it has a property characteristic of liquids—it sloshes around inside a container. From this model (that the can contains a liquid), you can make a prediction: If you punch a small hole in the bottom of the can, liquid will drip out.

The simple model we have made for the behavior of the contents of the tin can was the result of just one experiment, shaking the can. It led to only one rather obvious prediction. Nothing about the model helped us to understand the liquid itself. We shall investigate a particle model of matter to see if it will help us understand more about the nature of matter. But first we shall do an experiment with a "black box," which is a more complicated example than the tin can we have just described. The model you make to account for the behavior of the black box and the predictions you make from the model will make it easier for you to understand a model for matter.

The box you will use is clearly person-made (Figure 8.1). But you can experiment with it, organize the results of your experiment

Figure 8.1
A "black box."

into a model, and predict the results of new experiments. You can then test your predictions in ways quite similar to those we use when we investigate natural substances.

1† **In addition to enabling us to summarize and account for the facts we have obtained from observation and experiment, what should a good model do for us?**

2 **You have two eggs in the refrigerator. One is raw and the other is hard boiled, but you do not know which is which. You spin one egg and it spins easily. You spin the other and it comes to rest after a very few rotations.**
 a) Suggest a model that will account for the different behavior of the two eggs.
 b) On the basis of your model, what do you predict about the spinning of the two eggs if you boil both of them for 10 minutes?
 c) Check your prediction at home.

8.2 EXPERIMENT A BLACK BOX

All the boxes you and your classmates will use in this experiment are the same. The first step is to find out as much as you can about these boxes without pulling the rods out of the boxes and, of course, without opening them. Look at one of them, shake it lightly, tilt it back and forth in various directions, and listen carefully to the sounds. You will find it very useful to write down your observations. This will help you to compare notes with your classmates so that you can arrive at a model, make predictions, and test them.

Do all the experiments you can think of, short of pulling out the rods or opening the box. Try to imagine in a general way what is inside the box that could account for your observations. This will be your model for the box. Do not be distracted by details. Do not, for example, try to name the objects inside the box; only describe them by the properties that you have found in your experiments. If you hear something sliding on one of the rods, you could equally well describe it as "a washer" or "a ring"; but the important point is that it is something with a hole in it through which the rod passes.

After you and your classmates have made models that account for your observations, predict what will happen as you pull out a particular rod. Also predict how this will affect the results of the tests you performed earlier. (Be sure to write down your predictions so that you can check them.) Then you or one of your classmates can remove this rod—but do so from only one of the boxes. Pulling out one of the rods may change things enough to prevent you from checking your prediction of what would have happened had you pulled out another rod first. This is why only one box at a time should be used to test each prediction. If what happens confirms your prediction, you can use one of the other boxes to test your predictions about what would happen if you pulled out one of the other rods first. If, however, your first prediction was not confirmed, modify your model accordingly before experimenting further. Continue this process until you have arrived at a model in which you have confidence.

---

3 a) **In investigating the black box, you did certain things to it that you could easily undo. Give some examples.**
b) In investigating the characteristic properties of a substance, you can also do things that can easily be undone. Give some examples.
c) What did you do to the black box that you could not undo?
d) Does dissolving zinc in hydrochloric acid resemble any of the kinds of tests you mentioned in part (a) or part (c)?

8.3 THE ATOMIC MODEL OF MATTER

Let us now begin to build an atomic model for matter by reviewing some of the common properties of elements, compounds, and mixtures. The assumptions we introduce into the model must be able to account for these properties.

First, we know that different samples of an element have the same characteristic properties. To account for this, we shall assume that an element is made up of tiny particles of only one kind. We call these particles "atoms." Different elements are made up of different kinds of atoms. Even with a high-powered microscope we cannot see atoms, and so they must be very small and there must be very many of them in any sample large enough for us to examine.

Second, in those experiments in which we worked with more than one element at a time, we found two quite different kinds of substances, which we labeled "compounds" and "mixtures." You will recall that when elements react to form compounds, they combine only in a definite ratio. You saw evidence for this law of constant proportions in the burning of hydrogen with oxygen and in the synthesis of zinc chloride. Furthermore, the compound produced in each case showed every evidence of being a new, pure substance. It had its own fixed set of characteristic properties, usually quite different from the properties of the reacting elements. The characteristic properties of carbon dioxide, for example, are entirely different from those of the carbon and oxygen that combine to make it.

Mixtures of elements, on the other hand, can be made in widely varying proportions of the basic ingredients and therefore do not show a law of constant proportions. Furthermore, the characteristic properties of a mixture can be made to vary widely simply by varying the amounts of the elements being mixed together. And, at least some of the characteristic properties of the individual elements (for example, color, solubility, smell, ability to react with other substances) are usually present in the mixture; this is not true in the case of compounds.

We have clear evidence that the elements have not really disappeared when compounds and mixtures are formed. In both cases, the pure elements can be freed and returned to their original form. The hydrogen and oxygen that were burned together to form water can be recovered by electrolysis of water. Nitrogen and oxygen mixed together to form air can be separated into pure nitrogen and oxygen by liquefying the air and fractionally distilling it. Furthermore, even without separating the individual elements in a mixture or compound, we have some evidence that they are still present by observing their spectra. In the compound sodium chloride, for example, we can clearly detect the spectral lines of sodium.

We can account for all this behavior by assuming that in each of these processes, the atoms of the individual elements remain essentially unchanged. That is, neither their number nor their individual masses change. They only rearrange themselves. Note that with this assumption, the model guarantees that mass is conserved when we form mixtures and compounds and when we break them up.

To account for the law of constant proportions displayed by compounds, one more assumption must be added to our model. We must assume that when a compound is formed, each atom of one element attaches to a fixed number of atoms of the other elements in a pattern characteristic of the compound. A mixture apparently does not have such a characteristic pattern, and so the composition is not fixed.

According to our model, then, it is this attachment by atoms of different kinds to each other that is responsible for compounds having characteristic properties different from those of the elements of which they are made.

To get a better picture of what we believe is happening to individual atoms when a compound is formed, you can do the experiment described in the next section.

---

4 Suppose that M atoms of mercury combine with N atoms of oxygen to form mercury oxide.
   a) What total number of atoms would you expect there to be in the sample of mercury oxide produced?
   b) If the mercury oxide produced is then decomposed by heating to form gaseous mercury and oxygen, how many atoms of mercury and how many atoms of oxygen would you expect to find?
   c) Would your answers to (b) be different if you had condensed the samples of gas to liquid mercury and liquid oxygen?

8.4 "EXPERIMENT" FASTENERS AND RINGS: CONSTANT COMPOSITION

Since we cannot see atoms directly, the atomic model of matter may not appear real to you. This experiment is designed to help you illustrate some aspects of it.

You will be using two "elements." The atoms of element Fs are paper fasteners; the atoms of element R are rubber rings. Note that the fasteners are all alike, just as we assume that the atoms of one element are all alike. Similarly, all the rings are alike, though they differ from the fasteners because they are meant to represent atoms of another element (Figure 8.2). We can fit rings on fasteners to "synthesize" a "compound" of two elements. When we do this,

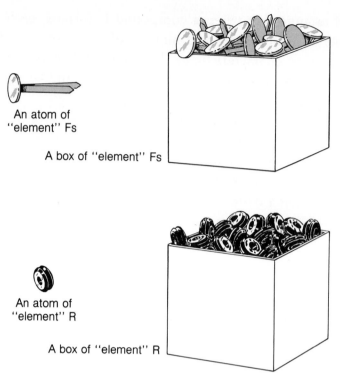

An atom of
"element" Fs

A box of "element" Fs

An atom of
"element" R

A box of "element" R

Figure 8.2
Paper fasteners can be used to represent the atoms of "element" Fs,
and rubber rings to represent the atoms of "element" R.

the number of rings and the number of fasteners and their individual masses do not change. This agrees with the model.

When you make a compound using these objects, you can think of the process as being similar to the formation of copper oxide from hot copper and the oxygen in the air. In that experiment, you worked with large numbers of atoms that you could not see individually. In this experiment, you will illustrate the process by using many visible "atoms" to form a sample of a compound.

Find the mass of all the Fs that you have been given. Make as much of the compound FsR as your supply of atoms allows by putting one ring on each fastener (Figure 8.3). When we write FsR, we mean a compound made up of one atom of Fs for every atom of R.

Figure 8.3
Making the "compound" FsR.

- What is the mass of the product you have synthesized?

If you have an excess of Fs, find its mass.

- How much Fs reacted with R?

- What is the ratio of the mass of R to the mass of product in your sample of the compound?

Compare your results with those of your classmates.

- Does the ratio of the mass of R to the mass of product depend on how big a sample you make?

- Does the model as illustrated by fasteners and rings agree with the law of constant proportions?

- Would the ratio have been the same if you had used heavier rings?

If you "decomposed" the compound you have made into pure Fs and R by taking the rings off the fasteners, you would get back all the atoms you started with.

- If you then measured the masses of the elements Fs and R that you got, would the model as illustrated by rings and fasteners agree with the law of conservation of mass?

5† Does the experiment with rubber rings and paper fasteners give you any information about the shape of an atom?

6 In the experiment on synthesis of water described in section 6.3, different amounts of hydrogen were mixed with the same amount of oxygen, and then the mixture was ignited by a spark. In the first case, there was some oxygen left over; in the second case, nearly all the oxygen and hydrogen reacted; and in the third case, hydrogen was left over. Describe the results of these experiments in terms of the atomic model of matter.

7 Suppose that element A can form a compound with element B but not with element C. Element B can form a compound with C. How would you choose fasteners, rings, and washers to represent these elements?

8 Describe the synthesis of zinc chloride (Experiment 6.4) in terms of fasteners, rings, and washers. (Hint: Hydrochloric acid contains hydrogen and chlorine.)

8.5 "EXPERIMENT" SOME OTHER COMPOUNDS OF Fs AND R

The compound FsR is only one of many that we can form from the elements Fs and R. An entirely different compound can be made from these elements by using two atoms of R for every atom of Fs. This new compound has the formula FsR_2 (Figure 8.4). The "$_2$" in the formula means that there are two atoms of R for every atom of Fs in the compound.

Figure 8.4
Making the "compound" FsR_2.

Make a quantity of the compound FsR_2, decompose it, and find the total mass of R that combined with the total mass of Fs.

- What mass of R would have combined with 100 g of Fs?

- Using the data from the preceding experiment, what mass of R would have combined with 100 g of Fs in the compound FsR?

- How do the quantities of R that combined with 100 g of Fs in the compounds FsR and FsR_2 compare?

- Does this ratio depend on the mass of the compounds you made?

Make a quantity of the compound FsR_3. Decompose it and determine the mass of R that combined with 100 g of Fs. Compare this mass of R in FsR_3 with the masses of R in FsR and FsR_2 that combine with 100 g of Fs.

9† The ratio of the mass of lead to the mass of oxygen in an oxide of lead is 13. How many grams of lead will combine with 100 g of oxygen?

10 You can make several "compounds" by gluing pennies (Pe) and nickels (Ni) together. The ratio of the mass of Ni to Pe in the compound NiPe is 1.6. What will be the ratio of the mass of Ni to Pe in the compound (a) Ni_2Pe, (b) Ni_3Pe, (c) $NiPe_2$?

8.6 A PREDICTION FROM THE ATOMIC MODEL OF MATTER

In the last two sections, you synthesized compounds from fasteners and rings. The ratio of the masses of the elements that combined to form a given compound was constant, regardless of the original masses of the elements used. Of course, instead of fasteners and rings, you could have used magnets and nails, or nickels and pennies glued together, or almost any pairs of things to represent two different kinds of atoms. The details of the shape, size, and color of our atoms were unimportant. The important point is that we imagine different kinds of particles that we can combine together.

The experiment you have just done allows us to make a prediction from the atomic model. Consider the results of the last fastener-and-ring experiment. You were asked to compare the masses of R that combine with 100 g of Fs in two compounds of these elements: FsR and FsR_2. You found this ratio of the masses of R to be close to 2. You could have predicted this because all the rings have the same mass, all the fasteners have the same mass, and the compound FsR contains only one ring for each fastener, whereas the other compound, FsR_2, contains two rings for every fastener.

What does the model predict about real compounds? Let us assume that we have two different compounds made only of the elements copper and chlorine. Suppose that one compound contains two atoms of chlorine for every atom of copper and the other compound contains only one atom of chlorine for every atom of copper. We expect the mass of chlorine combined with 100 g of copper in the first compound to be twice the mass of chlorine that is combined with 100 g of copper in the second compound.

Consider another possibility: One compound contains three atoms of chlorine for every atom of copper, and the other compound contains equal numbers of copper and chlorine atoms, as before. (This would resemble the relationship between FsR_3 and FsR.) The model predicts the mass of chlorine in the first compound to be three times as great as in the second for a given mass of copper.

11 Samples of two compounds containing only nuts and bolts were decomposed. A mass of 100 g of each yielded the following data.

Compound sample	Mass of bolts (g)	Mass of nuts (g)
1	80	20
2	67	33

a) **What mass of nuts would combine with 100 g of bolts in sample 1?**

b) **What mass of nuts would combine with 100 g of bolts in sample 2?**

c) **What is the ratio of the mass of nuts in sample 2 to the mass of nuts in sample 1 that would combine with 100 g of bolts?**

8.7 EXPERIMENT   TWO COMPOUNDS OF COPPER

Copper and chlorine do in fact form two different compounds. Both compounds are solids at room temperature. One is brown and has a melting point of 498°C. It has no boiling point because the liquid decomposes before it is hot enough to boil. The other compound of copper and chlorine is light green and has a melting point of 422°C and a boiling point of 1366°C. We shall investigate these two compounds to make a comparison between the mass of chlorine combined with 100 g of copper in one and the mass of chlorine combined with 100 g of copper in the other.

You will be placing a piece of aluminum in two solutions, each of which contains a measured mass of one of these compounds. In each case, the aluminum will replace the copper in the solution. The copper will precipitate, and you can separate it, dry it, and mass it. From the measured masses of the copper and the compounds, you can calculate the masses of chlorine that combine with 100 g of copper in the two compounds.

Find the mass of a watch glass as accurately as you can. Onto the watch glass put between 2 g and 4 g of the brown powder. Then mass very accurately the watch glass with the brown powder on it. Dissolve the powder in a beaker containing 25 cm³ of water, and heat the solution to around 60°C. Now add a piece of aluminum to the solution. Stirring the solution from time to time with a glass rod will hasten the reaction.

When all the copper has been removed from the compound, the solution will be colorless. The solution can then be boiled a few minutes to loosen any copper deposited on the aluminum. Agitating the aluminum in the solution will help break off any bits of copper sticking to it. It may be necessary to scrape the aluminum with a scoopula to remove all the copper. Now you can remove what is left of the piece of aluminum.

When the copper has sunk to the bottom, you can pour off most of the liquid without losing any copper. You can wash out any of the remaining solution by adding 50 cm³ of water and stirring thoroughly. To be sure none of the aluminum chloride solution remains, pour off the wash water once, add 50 cm³ of fresh water and stir, then pour off the water a second time. While washing, be sure to break up the copper chunks as much as possible with a glass rod. This will help remove any solution trapped in the spongy copper. If you wash it again with about 25 cm³ of alcohol or burner fuel, the copper will dry rapidly. (Alcohol evaporates quickly. Be sure no burners are being used while you wash the solid with alcohol.)

Now you can carefully scrape the copper onto the watch glass you massed earlier. To dry the copper, you can either let it stand overnight or place the watch glass over boiling water for 20 to 30 minutes. When you think the copper is dry, mass the watch glass with the copper, and then check the mass again after 10 minutes of additional heating to be sure the copper is dry.

- How can you tell if it is dry?

- What mass of copper did you get?

To see that the solid you have separated from the compound is copper, you can squeeze it into a lump and hammer it.

- Does the solid resemble copper?

- What was the mass of chlorine in the sample of brown powder you used?

- What mass of chlorine is combined with 100 g of copper in this compound?

Repeat the experiment you have just done, but this time use 2 g to 4 g of the light-green compound of copper.

- What is the mass of chlorine combined with 100 g of copper in this compound?

- How does the mass of chlorine combined with 100 g of copper in the brown compound compare with the mass of chlorine combined with 100 g of copper in the light-green compound?

- What do the results of this experiment tell you about the number of chlorine atoms combined with one copper atom in the two compounds?

---

12 In the experiment you have just done, how would the value of the mass of chlorine combined with 100 g of copper in the brown powder have been altered if this powder had not been thoroughly dried before massing?

13 In the case of the brown powder, suppose that some copper had been left in the beaker after the wet copper was transferred to the watch glass. How would this error have affected the results of the experiment?

14 A student repeated the experiment with the brown copper chloride several times, and each time he used the same strip of aluminum. In his last determination, he found that there was no aluminum left to recover. How would this affect his value for the mass of chlorine combined with 100 g of copper in the last determination?

8.8   THE LAW OF MULTIPLE PROPORTIONS

There are other combinations of fasteners and rings that we can put together to illustrate possible compounds. Two of these, along with two of the combinations you have already made, are shown in Table 8.1. In each case, we have calculated the mass of rings that would combine with 100 g of fasteners. The ratio of the masses is expressed as a ratio of small whole numbers.

Table 8.1

"Compound formula"	Mass M of R combined with 100 g of Fs (g)	Mass ratios
FsR	$M_1 = 29.3$	–
FsR_2	$M_2 = 58.6$	$\dfrac{M_2}{M_1} = \dfrac{2}{1}$
Fs_2R	$M_3 = 14.7$	$\dfrac{M_3}{M_1} = \dfrac{1}{2}$
Fs_2R_3	$M_4 = 44.0$	$\dfrac{M_4}{M_1} = \dfrac{3}{2}$

With fasteners and rings, we have illustrated some possible combinations of elements; now let us look at some actual compounds. Nitrogen and oxygen combine to form several oxides with distinctly different properties. In Table 8.2(a), the oxides are identified by their boiling points. They are listed in order of increasing mass of oxygen that combined with 100 g of nitrogen.

Table 8.2(a)

Oxide	Boiling point (°C)	Mass M of oxygen combined with 100 g of nitrogen (g)	Mass ratio	Possible formula
1	−88.6	$M_1 = 57.2$	−	NO
2	−151.1	$M_2 = 114.3$	$\dfrac{M_2}{M_1} = \dfrac{2}{1}$	NO_2
3	3.5	$M_3 = 171.5$	$\dfrac{M_3}{M_1} = \dfrac{3}{1}$	NO_3
4	21.3	$M_4 = 228.6$	$\dfrac{M_4}{M_1} = \dfrac{4}{1}$	NO_4

The ratios of these masses are expressed by small whole numbers. The numbers themselves depend on which mass we choose to be in the denominator in the fourth column of Table 8.2(a). Had we chosen M_2 to be in the denominator, we would have gotten different ratios and different formulas (Table 8.2[b]). But these ratios

Table 8.2(b)

Oxide	Boiling point (°C)	Mass M of oxygen combined with 100 g of nitrogen (g)	Mass ratio	Possible formula
1	−88.6	$M_1 = 57.2$	$\dfrac{M_1}{M_2} = \dfrac{1}{2}$	N_2O
2	−151.1	$M_2 = 114.3$	−	NO
3	3.5	$M_3 = 171.5$	$\dfrac{M_3}{M_2} = \dfrac{3}{2}$	N_2O_3
4	21.3	$M_4 = 228.6$	$\dfrac{M_4}{M_2} = 2$	NO_2

also are expressed by small whole numbers. The fact that the ratios are expressed by small whole numbers does not depend on how we calculate them. This is good evidence that elements do combine as though they were made up of individual particles.

Oxygen is known to combine in different mass ratios with many elements besides nitrogen. However, it is by no means the only element that behaves this way. Table 8.3 shows other pairs of elements and their compounds. Note that the mass ratios in the last column are all expressed by small whole numbers. The results of the experiment you did with the chlorides of copper, as well as those of many other experiments on the composition of compounds, suggest the following generalization. For any two elements that form more than one compound, the ratio of the masses of one element that combine with a fixed mass of the other element is expressed by a small whole number. This generalization is known as the law of multiple proportions.

Table 8.3

Compound	Composition	Mass ratios
1	100 g iron, 127 g chlorine	$\dfrac{127}{191} = \dfrac{2}{3}$
2	100 g iron, 191 g chlorine	
1	100 g carbon, 33.3 g hydrogen	$\dfrac{33.3}{25.0} = \dfrac{4}{3}$
2	100 g carbon, 25.0 g hydrogen	
1	100 g phosphorus, 344 g chlorine	$\dfrac{344}{573} = \dfrac{3}{5}$
2	100 g phosphorus, 573 g chlorine	
3	100 g phosphorus, 229 g chlorine	$\dfrac{573}{229} = \dfrac{5}{2}$

In deriving the law of multiple proportions from the atomic model of matter, we have been following in the footsteps of John Dalton (1766–1844). He did not use fasteners and rings in making his predictions, but he definitely thought in terms of two kinds of particles. He then found experimental evidence for the law of multiple proportions by analyzing compounds containing only oxygen and nitrogen (Table 8.2) and compounds containing only hydrogen and carbon.

Let us emphasize once more that we did not have to use fasteners and rings to predict the law of multiple proportions. We could just as well have used pennies and nickels stuck together with glue, because all pennies are alike, all nickels are alike, and nickels are different from pennies.

You have now studied two laws concerning the formation of compounds: the law of constant proportions (section 6.5) and the law of multiple proportions. The first law applies to a single compound of any two given elements. To describe the formation of more than one compound by the same two elements, we need the second law. Thus the law of multiple proportions is an extension of the law of constant proportions.

When two elements can form more than one compound, it is often difficult to synthesize one of the compounds without forming some of the others at the same time. The relative amounts of the various compounds depend on the relative quantities of the elements we start with, the temperature, and other conditions. In such cases, experiments will yield different ratios for the elements in what can be mistaken for a single compound. Part of the difficulty of originally establishing the law of constant proportions was the formation of more than one compound by the same two elements. This is one of the reasons why the combining of copper and sulfur seemed to violate the law of constant proportions. (See section 6.5.) Another complication occurs when the sulfur is present in excess. The compounds formed dissolve in the excess sulfur to form "frozen" solutions. This may give the material the appearance of a uniform solid, which is easily mistaken for a single compound. It is very difficult to separate the newly formed components from a "frozen" solution.

Note that the law of multiple proportions does not tell us what specific ratios to expect from any given pair of elements that form more than one compound. It states only: If two elements, A and B, form two or more compounds, then the ratio of the masses of A combining with a given mass of B will be given by the ratio of two small whole numbers. Some pairs of elements form several compounds, whereas others form only one or even none (helium, for example, is not known to combine with any other element).

There must be some important differences between the atoms of the various elements to account for their different behavior in forming compounds.

15† What is the ratio of the mass of chlorine that combines with 100 g of phosphorus in phosphorus trichloride to the mass of chlorine that combines with 100 g of phosphorus in diphosphorus tetrachloride (Table 8.3)?

16 From the data given below for compounds of lead and oxygen, calculate the ratios in the last column. Do these ratios agree with the law of multiple proportions?

Compound	Mass M of oxygen combined with 100 g of lead (g)	Mass ratio
Lead(I) oxide	$M_1 = 3.86$	—
Lead(II) oxide	$M_2 = 7.72$	$\dfrac{M_2}{M_1}$
Lead(III) oxide	$M_3 = 11.58$	$\dfrac{M_3}{M_1}$
Lead(IV) oxide	$M_4 = 15.44$	$\dfrac{M_4}{M_1}$

17 Two compounds containing only carbon and oxygen are decomposed. A mass of 100 g of compound I contains 43 g of carbon, and 100 g of compound II contains 27 g of carbon.
a) What is the ratio of the mass of carbon to the mass of oxygen for each compound?
b) If compound II has the formula CO_2, what is a possible formula for compound I?

8.9 MOLECULES

So far, we have used the atomic model in a rather vague way to describe the formation of compounds: In every compound made of two elements, A and B, the atoms arrange themselves in such a way that for each atom of A there are one or more atoms of B. We have not yet attempted to describe exactly how the large numbers of these are arranged in a sample of a compound. Figure 8.5 shows several possibilities for a compound containing equal numbers of atoms of two elements. In Figure 8.5(*a*), the atoms of the two elements are clearly paired off, with space between each pair. In Figure 8.5(*b*), the atoms form clusters of four. In Figures 8.5(*c*) and (*d*), we can no longer distinguish groups or clusters containing a fixed number of atoms. In Figure 8.5(*c*), there is no particular order to the atoms, whereas in Figure 8.5(*d*) they are arranged in neat rows. Which of these pictures fits the arrangement of atoms in real compounds? To answer this question, we must look into what we already know about the behavior of matter in bulk.

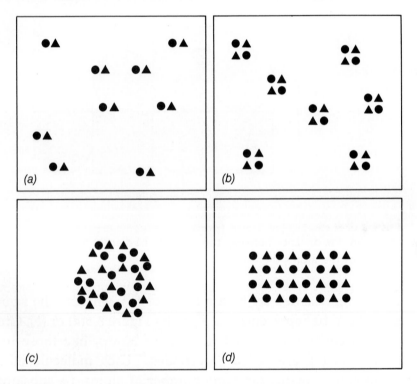

Figure 8.5
Possible arrangements of the atoms of two elements in a compound
that contains equal numbers of each kind of atom.

Anybody who has ever used a bicycle pump knows that it is quite easy to compress air into a volume much smaller than the volume it originally occupied. The same is true for all gases. But try to reduce the volume of a small crystal of sodium chloride even by 1 percent. You might try squeezing it in a cylinder with a piston, but you will not be able to do it without special equipment that can exert very large pressures. A cube of copper will behave similarly.

While gases are quite compressible, solids are almost incompressible. We can account for this by assuming that atoms behave like little hard objects whose size remains fixed. In a solid, the atoms are close together; they are all "touching" one another. This means that the distance between the centers of the atoms equals the size of the atoms themselves (Figure 8.6). Such a picture suggests that solids are hard to compress. In a gas, on the other hand, the atoms do not touch one another. They are far apart in relation to their size and can easily be pushed closer together to occupy a smaller volume (Figure 8.7). Thus, the solid or liquid compound AB

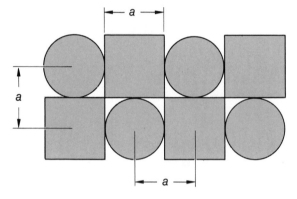

Figure 8.6
In a solid, the distance between the centers of adjacent atoms equals
the size of the atoms themselves.

can be represented by Figure 8.5(*c*) or (*d*), whereas the same compound can be represented as a gas by Figure 8.5(*a*) or (*b*). Groups or clusters containing a fixed number of atoms, like those in Figure 8.5(*a*) and (*b*), are called "molecules." Each molecule of a given compound contains the same number of atoms. (A substance with more than one kind of molecule could not be a pure substance.)

Compounds are not the only substances made of molecules. The atoms of a single element can also form clusters or molecules, with only one kind of atom in each cluster. In this course we do not go into the analysis of the many experiments and the long chain of arguments that are necessary to decide the numbers of various kinds of atoms in the molecules of different gases. We shall simply state the results for some of the substances we have used as illustrations. In gaseous hydrogen, the atoms cluster together in pairs; thus the correct molecular formula of hydrogen gas is H_2. The atoms of gaseous iodine also cluster together in pairs. A molecule of water vapor (H_2O) consists of two atoms of hydrogen and one of oxygen,

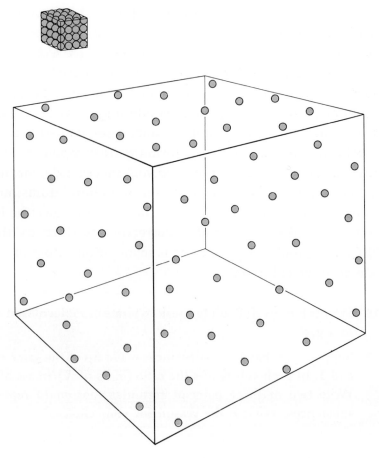

Figure 8.7
The large box represents a volume of helium gas at atmospheric pressure and room temperature. The spheres in the box represent helium atoms. The small box shows the volume occupied by the helium atoms in the large box when the helium is liquefied.

and a molecule of carbon dioxide (CO_2) is a cluster of two oxygen atoms and one carbon atom. The atoms of helium gas (He) do not form clusters.

While every sample of a given compound must contain the same elements in the same ratio by mass, the reverse is not necessarily true. That is, two substances having the same elements in the same ratio by mass need not be the same compound. For example, the two oxides of nitrogen NO_2 and N_2O_4 have the same ratio of nitrogen and oxygen. However, the molecules of NO_2 have three atoms and those of N_2O_4 have six atoms. The two oxides are distinctly different compounds. Here is another example: two compounds of carbon and hydrogen, namely ethyne and benzene, have the same mass ratio of carbon to hydrogen, but have very different properties. A molecule of ethyne consists of four atoms, C_2H_2, and a molecule of benzene consists of twelve atoms, C_6H_6.

When the atoms of a solid are arranged as in Figure 8.6, it is meaningless to talk about clusters or molecules unless we wish to consider such an arrangement as one huge molecule. The only information a formula gives us in such cases is the fixed ratio of the numbers of the various atoms forming the compound. Thus the formula NaCl, when applied to solid sodium chloride, means only that the crystal contains equal numbers of sodium atoms and chlorine atoms. However, a molecule of sodium chloride gas (the liquid boils at 1400°C!) does exist and is correctly described by the formula NaCl. Each molecule of the gas is made of one atom of sodium and one atom of chlorine.

---

18   Why is it more difficult to speak in terms of molecules in a solid than in a gas?

19   Suppose you have two substances made up of the same elements, X and Y. In both substances the ratio (mass of X)/(mass of Y) is 0.45. Write two or three pairs of formulas that could represent these substances. What is the reason for your choices?

8.10   RELATIVE ATOMIC MASSES: THE MOLE

A mass of 119 g of carbon combines with 10.0 g of hydrogen to form 129 g of ethyne. By mass, the ratio of carbon to hydrogen is therefore:

$$\frac{119 \text{ g}}{10.0 \text{ g}} = 11.9$$

How is this ratio related to the ratio of the mass of one carbon atom to the mass of one hydrogen atom?

In general, for any element,

$$\text{Mass of one atom} = \frac{\text{mass of sample}}{\text{number of atoms in sample}}.$$

Let us apply this relation to the 119 g of carbon and the 10.0 g of hydrogen that form 129 g of ethyne.

Mass of one carbon atom

$$= \frac{119 \text{ g}}{\text{number of carbon atoms in 119 g of carbon}}$$

Mass of one hydrogen atom

$$= \frac{10.0 \text{ g}}{\text{number of hydrogen atoms in 10.0 g of hydrogen}}$$

At this point we know neither of the numbers of atoms that appear in the denominator of the last two equations. Therefore, we cannot use these equations to find the mass of one atom. However, the formula for a molecule of ethyne, C_2H_2, tells us that each molecule of ethyne contains two atoms of carbon and two atoms of hydrogen. Therefore, any sample of ethyne, no matter how many molecules are in it, contains *equal* numbers of carbon atoms and hydrogen atoms:

Number of carbon atoms in 119 g
$$= \text{number of hydrogen atoms in 10.0 g}$$

This information is still insufficient to find the mass of one atom. But it is enough to find the ratio of the mass of one carbon atom to the mass of one hydrogen atom. In this ratio the unknown but equal number of atoms cancels out. Hence,

$$\frac{\text{Mass of one carbon atom}}{\text{Mass of one hydrogen atom}} = \frac{119 \text{ g}}{10.0 \text{ g}} = 11.9.$$

Here is the same reasoning applied to water. When water is decomposed, one gets 792 g of oxygen for every 100 g of hydrogen. Applying the general relation between the mass of an atom and the mass of a sample to this case gives us:

Mass of one oxygen atom

$$= \frac{792 \text{ g}}{\text{number of oxygen atoms in 792 g of oxygen}}.$$

Mass of one hydrogen atom

$$= \frac{100 \text{ g}}{\text{number of hydrogen atoms in 100 g of hydrogen}}.$$

The formula for water is H_2O. That is, every sample of water contains half as many oxygen atoms as hydrogen atoms. Specifically,

$$\text{Number of oxygen atoms in 792 g} = \frac{1}{2} \times (\text{number of hydrogen atoms in 100 g}).$$

Thus, the number of oxygen atoms in 2 × 792 g, or 1,584 g, of oxygen equals the number of hydrogen atoms in 100 g of hydrogen. Therefore:

$$\frac{\text{Mass of one oxygen atom}}{\text{Mass of one hydrogen atom}} = \frac{1,584}{100} = 15.84$$

Most elements combine with either hydrogen or oxygen. Once the molecular formulas for their compounds have been determined, the ratios of the atomic masses of these elements can be determined.

The hydrogen atom turns out to be the lightest atom. It would be natural to set its mass as one atomic mass unit and express all atomic masses in terms of the mass of the hydrogen atom. On this mass scale, the carbon atom would have a mass of 11.9.

For a variety of reasons it has been generally agreed to set the mass of the carbon atom on the relative scale at exactly 12.00 unified atomic mass units (u). This makes the mass of an oxygen atom 16.0 u (instead of 15.84). The mass of a hydrogen atom becomes 1.01 u. A list of atomic masses (relative to carbon as 12 u) is shown in Table 8.4.

From Table 8.4, the ratio of the mass of a chlorine atom to the mass of a hydrogen atom is 35.5/1.01 = 35.15. The ratio of the mass of ten chlorine atoms to the mass of ten hydrogen atoms is also 35.15. So is the ratio of any equal number of atoms of these two elements. Hence, a sample of chlorine and a sample of hydrogen with a mass ratio of 35.15 will have the *same* number of atoms, whatever that number may be.

In particular, from Table 8.4, 35.5 g of chlorine contains the same number of atoms as 1.01 g of hydrogen, or as 12.0 g of carbon. In fact, a sample of any element in the table with a mass in grams equal to the mass listed in the table has the same number of atoms as 12.0 g of carbon. This number is called a "mole."

Table 8.4

Element	Symbol	Mass of one atom (u)	Element	Symbol	Mass of one atom (u)
Aluminum	Al	27.0	Mercury	Hg	201
Calcium	Ca	40.1	Nickel	Ni	58.7
Carbon	C	12.0	Nitrogen	N	14.0
Chlorine	Cl	35.5	Oxygen	O	16.0
Copper	Cu	63.5	Phosphorus	P	31.0
Gold	Au	197	Potassium	K	39.1
Helium	He	4.00	Sodium	Na	23.0
Hydrogen	H	1.01	Sulfur	S	32.1
Iodine	I	127	Thorium	Th	232
Iron	Fe	55.8	Tin	Sn	119
Lead	Pb	207	Uranium	U	238
Lithium	Li	6.94	Zinc	Zn	65.4

Since elements form compounds by the combination of atoms, it is convenient to know how much of an element is needed to combine with another element in a given atomic ratio. Measuring the quantities of the elements in moles provides this information. For example, consider the burning of coal in air. (Coal is mostly carbon.) The reaction can be described as

$$C + O_2 \longrightarrow CO_2.$$

That is, one mole of carbon atoms combines with one mole of oxygen molecules (or two moles of oxygen atoms) to form one mole of carbon dioxide. With the aid of Table 8.4, we can state that 12.0 g of carbon combined with 32.0 g of oxygen to form 44.0 g of carbon dioxide.

The mole is defined as the number of carbon atoms in 12.0 g of carbon. What is this number? The answer to this question will come in Chapter 11, where a method of counting atoms is described.

20 (a) How many moles of copper atoms are in 63.5 g of copper?
    (b) What is the ratio of the number of sodium atoms in 46.0 g of sodium to the number of lithium atoms in 6.94 g of lithium?

21† What is the mass of one mole of water molecules?

22 Chlorine molecules are made up of two atoms (Cl_2). What is the mass of a mole of chlorine molecules?

23 Suppose in Experiment 6.1 you had decomposed two moles of sodium chlorate ($NaClO_3$) molecules.
    (a) How many moles of oxygen atoms would have been released?
    (b) How many moles of oxygen molecules would have been released?

8.11   RADIOACTIVE ELEMENTS AND THE ATOMIC MODEL

The basic idea in the atomic model of matter, as we have developed it, is this: In forming mixtures and compounds, the numbers of different kinds of atoms and their individual masses do not change. In this chapter, we have seen the usefulness of this idea. But what about radioactive decay?

We can extend our model to include radioactivity by assuming that in radioactive decay, an atom of the decaying element splits into two atoms—one of each of the new elements being formed (lead and helium, in the case of polonium). This assumption does not really contradict our basic idea that the number of atoms remains fixed. That basic idea still applies to such processes as melting, evaporating, mixing, forming compounds, and breaking them up. The one exception is the special process of radioactive decay. The assumption that an atom undergoing radioactive decay splits into two atoms is forced upon us by our observation of the process.

This state of affairs may not seem entirely satisfactory, but it is a common situation in the development of science. No sooner do we arrive at a model that seems to put our knowledge of nature in order than we begin to discover its limitations. We find that further experiments do not fulfill the predictions based on the new theory, and so we must modify and expand it.

For Home, Desk, and Lab

24 Think again of the sealed tin can referred to in section 8.1. You are not allowed to pierce the can or break it open. What would you predict about its behavior if (a) you lowered the temperature sufficiently or (b) you raised the temperature sufficiently?

25 While doing Experiment 8.2: A Black Box, why were you not permitted to open the box and look inside?

26 Which of the following are *parts* of our atomic model of matter? Which may be used as *illustrations* of the model?
a) Matter is made up of very tiny particles, much too small to be seen.
b) A paint sprayer will deposit more particles the longer it is operated.
c) Atoms of the same element are all alike.
d) Two rubber rings combine with one fastener to form FsR_2.
e) Atoms of two different elements may combine to form compounds.
f) Atoms of two different elements may combine in different ratios to form different compounds.
g) Marbles can be stacked in a box to represent a solid.

27 A mass of 16 g of oxygen combines with 63.5 g of copper to form CuO.
a) What is the ratio of the mass of copper to the mass of oxygen?
b) What is the ratio of the mass of copper to the mass of oxygen in Cu_2O?

28 In your own words state the law of multiple proportions.

29 Carbon can combine with chlorine to form three different compounds, CCl_4, C_2Cl_4, and C_2Cl_6. If the ratio of the mass of carbon to chlorine in CCl_4 is 0.286, what is the ratio of the mass of carbon to that of chlorine in the other two compounds?

30 Suppose that 6×10^6 atoms of hydrogen combine with 2×10^6 atoms of nitrogen and form 2×10^6 molecules of ammonia. How many atoms of hydrogen and how many atoms of nitrogen would there be in each molecule of ammonia?

31 How does the atomic model of matter help us to account for (a) the law of constant proportions, (b) the law of multiple proportions, and (c) the law of conservation of mass?

32 Four students suggested the following pairs of formulas for the two chlorides of copper.

Brown Chloride	Green Chloride
$CuCl_2$	$CuCl$
$CuCl$	Cu_2Cl
Cu_3Cl_2	$CuCl$
Cu_3Cl_4	Cu_3Cl_2

a) Which pair or pairs are possible formulas for these compounds?
b) Can you decide which pair gives the correct formulas for the chlorides of copper?

33 Refer to Table 3.1 on page 63.
a) About how large a cube of copper contains a mole of copper atoms?
b) About how large a volume of water contains a mole of water molecules?
c) About how large a volume of oxygen at atmospheric pressure and room temperature contains a mole of oxygen molecules?

34 In Experiment 6.1: Decomposition of Sodium Chlorate, suppose you actually decomposed 5 g of sodium chlorate.
a) How many moles would this be?
b) How many moles of oxygen molecules would be released?
c) Refer to Table 3.1. How many test tubes (35 cm^3 each) would be needed to collect all the oxygen?

35 In Experiment 6.4: Synthesis of Zinc Chloride, you investigated the composition of zinc chloride. Class data showed that the ratio (mass of zinc)/(mass of zinc chloride) was close to 0.48. What must be the simplest formula for zinc chloride? Use Table 8.4.

 Theme for a Short Essay

In or around your house are devices that do certain things. You know how to use them but you do not know how they work. For you, such devices are "black boxes." Choose one of these devices, describe in detail what it does when you do things to it, and explain why it is a "black box" to you.

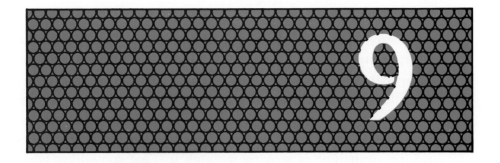

Electric Charge

9.1 INTRODUCTION

In Chapter 6 you used electricity to decompose water. Now we shall come back to this use and examine the connection between electricity and matter.

Figure 9.1 shows the apparatus used in Chapter 6 for the decomposition of water. With only one of the electrodes connected to the battery, no water decomposes. Nothing happens unless both electrodes are connected to the terminals of the battery.

Figure 9.1
Apparatus used for the decomposition of water in Chapter 6.

187

Any household electrical appliance—be it a light bulb, a motor, or a television set—has two contacts which have to be plugged in to get the device to operate.

This common characteristic, that an electrical apparatus must have two wires connecting it to a source of electricity, gave rise in the eighteenth century to the idea that when an electrical device is working something is moving through it. That something is called electric charge. When you pull out a plug, turn off a switch, or disconnect a battery, the flow of electric charge stops, and with it the operation of the apparatus.

The idea of a flowing electric charge is quite attractive, because it permits us to draw in our minds a mental picture which may eventually lead to a useful model. To develop the intuitive idea of a flowing electric charge into a model, we must find a way to measure the quantity of electric charge that flows through a bulb, a motor, or any other device. This situation resembles the one we encountered at the beginning of this course. We felt that there was more substance in a rock than in a pebble, but we needed the balance to enable us to make a quantitative comparison. But, while we could see the rock and the pebble directly, we cannot see electric charge either at rest or in motion. We have to look for an effect produced by moving charge which can be measured quantitatively. You have used such indirect methods many times before, probably without noticing it. For example, you cannot see temperature directly. To measure temperature, we use the fact that substances expand when heated, and we can construct various kinds of thermometers using thermal expansion. We shall use a similar method to build a charge meter.

1† **Which of the following quantities did you measure directly and which did you measure indirectly?**
   a) **Density of a solid in Experiment 3.7.**
   b) **Mass of metal cube in Experiment 3.7.**
   c) **Density of a gas in Experiment 3.10.**
   d) **Mass of chlorine in Experiment 8.7: Two Compounds of Copper.**

2 **What do you think an electric switch does?**

3 **Some lights used on trucks and automobiles are mounted by means of a metal bracket on the car body. These lights have only one wire, instead of two, to be connected to a switch and battery. How do you explain the operation of such a light?**

9.2 A MEASURE FOR THE QUANTITY OF CHARGE

In the experiment on the decomposition of water (section 6.2), you noted that the longer the time the electrodes are connected to the battery, the greater the volume of both gases produced. This suggests that more charge must have flowed through the apparatus when it was connected for a longer time. Thus it seems reasonable to use the quantity of either gas produced in the reaction as a measure of the quantity of electric charge that passes through the water. We shall choose the quantity of hydrogen, since we get twice as much of this gas as we do of oxygen, and this makes it easier to detect small quantities of charge. This apparatus, which we shall use as a charge meter, we shall refer to as a "hydrogen cell." It is constructed as shown in Figure 9.2. Notice that since we shall not be measuring the amount of oxygen, we have made no provision to collect it.

A source of electricity, such as a battery or a wall outlet, and one or more electrical devices connected to the source make up what

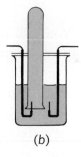

(b)

Figure 9.2
(a) Apparatus for decomposing water. The electrode at the right, at which oxygen is given off, is outside the test tube as shown in (b), so that only hydrogen is collected.

is called an electric circuit. If we want to know how much charge flows through a given part of an electric circuit (Figure 9.3[a] is an example), we break the circuit at that place and insert the hydrogen cell (Figure 9.3[b]). The amount of hydrogen collected tells us how much charge passed through the cell.

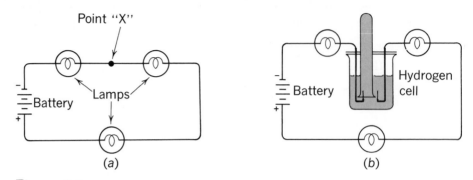

Figure 9.3
To measure the charge that flows past point X in the circuit shown in (a), the circuit is broken, and a hydrogen cell is inserted as shown in (b).

You will recall that volume is not a reliable measure of the quantity of matter, particularly in the case of a gas, since a gas expands and contracts appreciably as the pressure and the temperature change. Thus, to be accurate, we should measure the quantity of electric charge in terms of the mass, rather than the volume, of hydrogen collected in the test tube. But we can be quite sure that the temperature and pressure of the hydrogen are nearly the same all over the classroom for a short time. Therefore, as long as we are interested only in comparing quantities of charge measured almost at the same time, we can be satisfied with simply comparing the volumes of hydrogen collected in the test tubes of different hydrogen cells. We can choose any convenient volume of hydrogen in a test tube as our unit of electric charge. We shall use for our unit the charge needed to produce 1.0 cm^3 of hydrogen.

4† An electrolytic cell for producing hydrogen and oxygen is allowed to run for 5 minutes, and then the battery terminals are reversed. It now runs for an additional 5 minutes.
   a) Does the same quantity of charge flow in each 5-minute interval?
   b) What is the ratio of the volume of gas in one tube to the volume of gas in the other?

9.3 EXPERIMENT HYDROGEN CELLS AND LIGHT BULBS

If charge flows around the electric circuit in Figure 9.4, how will the volumes of hydrogen that will collect in the two hydrogen cells compare? Check your prediction by connecting two hydrogen cells, a battery, and a flashlight bulb as shown.

In order to collect hydrogen and not oxygen, be sure that the electrode under the test tube in each of the cells is connected to the wire which leads to the negative (−) terminal of the battery.

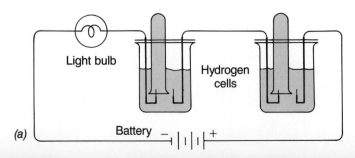

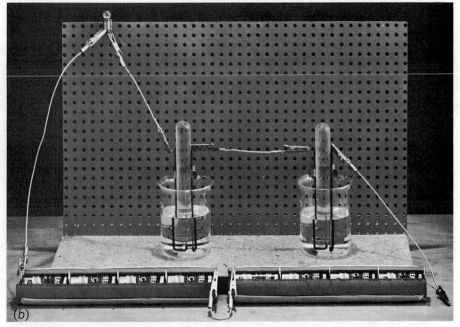

Figure 9.4
(a) A diagram of two hydrogen cells and a light bulb connected in series to a battery of flashlight cells. (b) A photograph of the actual connections to the apparatus. The end of the battery at the left is the negative (−) terminal; the end at the right is the positive (+) terminal. Note that the negative terminal of the battery is connected, through the light bulb, to the hydrogen-producing electrode in the left-hand cell. The wire from the other electrode of this cell goes to the hydrogen-producing electrode of the right-hand cell.

Using a battery of eight flashlight cells, collect hydrogen gas until the water level has dropped about 10 cm in one of the tubes.

After disconnecting the battery, mark the water level in each tube with a small rubber band or a grease pencil. You can use a graduated cylinder to measure the volume of gas collected in each test tube.

- Do your results agree with your prediction?

Now, rearrange the apparatus so that you can measure the charge that flows both into and out of the light bulb (Figure 9.5).

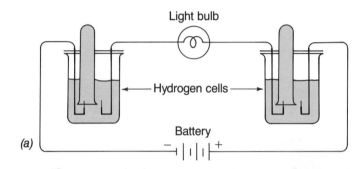

Figure 9.5

(*a*) The same circuit as shown in Figure 9.4(*a*), except that the light bulb is now between the two hydrogen cells so that both the charge entering the bulb and that leaving the bulb can be measured. (*b*) A photograph of the connections to the apparatus.

- How will the gas volumes in the two hydrogen cells compare in this circuit?
- Do your results confirm your prediction?

9.4 EXPERIMENT FLOW OF CHARGE AT DIFFERENT POINTS IN A CIRCUIT

The circuits shown in Figures 9.6 and 9.7 (pages 194 and 195) are slightly more complex than the simple *series* circuits shown in Figure 9.4. They are branched or *parallel* circuits with the light bulb inserted at different points. Investigate the charge flowing in each of the circuits. Again, in each case allow charge to flow until the liquid level in the test tube in the cell on the right falls about 10 cm.

- What do you predict the liquid levels will be in the other tubes?
- What is the relation between the amounts of charge flowing in different parts of the circuit?

---

5 A student connects to a battery a series circuit containing a hydrogen cell followed by a light bulb which is followed by another hydrogen cell. He obtains twice as much gas in one test tube as in the other. How could this be explained?

6 Each of two students connects up the circuit shown in Figure 9.6(a) and both collect gas for the same time interval. One of the students is unaware of the fact that his connections to the battery are the reverse of those shown in Figure 9.6(a). How would the charge he measured, in cm³ of gas, compare with the charge measured by the student who connected the circuit correctly?

7 Two identical light bulbs are connected to a battery as shown in Figure A. How does the charge flowing in one minute past point A compare with that flowing past points B and C?

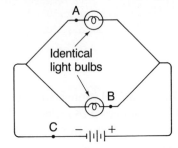

Figure A
For problem 7

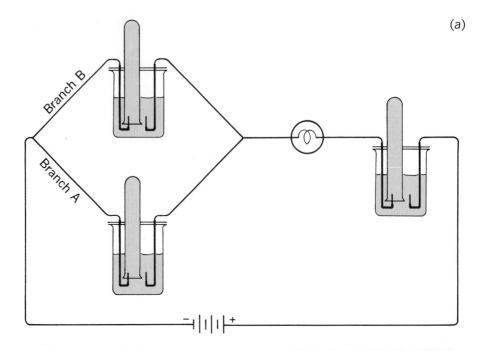

(a)

(b)

Figure 9.6

(a) Two hydrogen cells in parallel connected to a light bulb and a third hydrogen cell which are connected in series. (b) Apparatus connected according to the circuit in (a). The two hydrogen cells connected in parallel are on the left.

(a)

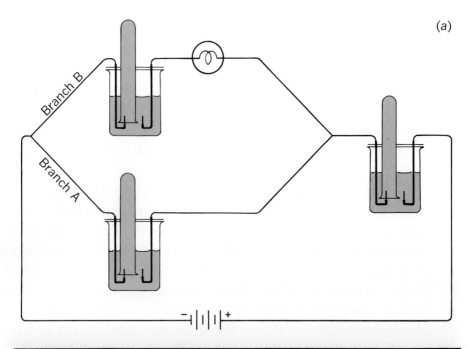

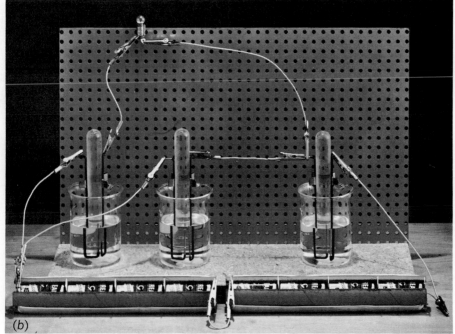

(b)

Figure 9.7

(a) The same circuit as in Figure 9.6(a), but with the light bulb in one of the branches of the parallel circuit. (b) The apparatus connected according to the circuit in (a). The light bulb and the hydrogen cell on the extreme left are connected in series and make up branch B of the parallel part of the circuit.

9.5 THE CONSERVATION OF ELECTRIC CHARGE

In the preceding section you examined the quantity of charge that passed through different parts of several electric circuits during a given time. The circuits were rather simple ones; besides the battery, hydrogen cells, and some wire, they contained only a small electric bulb. In all cases the results were consistent with the idea that the same amount of charge passed through all devices connected in series without being consumed.

What about a more complicated circuit—for example, one which also contains an electric motor and two radios (Figure 9.8)? Numerous circuits containing various kinds of electrical devices have been examined, always with the same results. As long as all devices are connected in series, one after another, the same quantity of charge passes through each device. When two or more wires branch off from one point, the sum of the charges passing through all parallel sections equals the charge that flows through the wire before the branch point. In this case as well, no electric charge is lost and none is created. Many different kinds of experiments have added support to the idea that no charge is created and no charge is destroyed.

The results of these experiments resemble those of the experiments investigating the change of mass in various processes (sections 2.10–2.14). Within the accuracy of the measurements, your own as well as those of others, we concluded that the total mass did not change in these reactions. We generalized these results into a

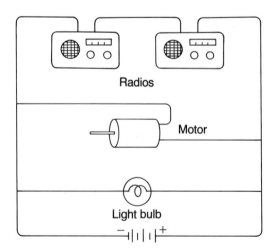

Figure 9.8
A circuit made up of two radios in series connected in parallel with an electric motor and a light bulb.

law, the law of conservation of mass. The fact that within the accuracy of the measurements electric charge is neither created nor destroyed when it flows around a circuit suggests a similar generalization. It is known as the law of the conservation of electric charge: electric charge is never destroyed or created.

By now we have great confidence in the law of conservation of charge. When we encounter a situation where the law seems to be violated, we check very carefully for some ways by which charge may have flowed unnoticed. For example, if a wire carrying electric charge is supported by poorly insulating materials, some charge will leak through the insulator and return to the battery through a different path. If this is not taken into account, it will look like a violation of charge conservation. But when the leaking charge is measured, conservation is found to hold.

---

8 Would the bulb in Figure 9.6 have glowed with more, less, or the same brightness if it had been placed between the battery and the hydrogen cell on the right?

9† Three hydrogen cells are connected to a battery as shown in Figure B. When 30 cm³ of hydrogen is collected in tube 1, it is observed that tube 2 has 20 cm³ of hydrogen. What is the volume of hydrogen in tube 3?

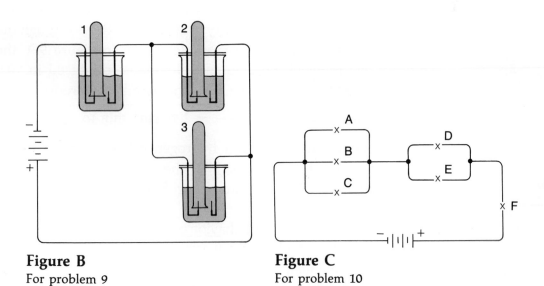

Figure B
For problem 9

Figure C
For problem 10

10 Identical hydrogen cells are inserted at the points marked "X" of the circuit shown in Figure C. Compare the volumes of hydrogen gas that would be collected in the cells at A, D, and F in equal times.

11 In Experiment 9.4: Flow of Charge at Different Points in a Circuit, suppose that some gas escaped unnoticed while being collected in the test tube in branch A of Figure 9.7(a). Would the results obtained suggest that charge was created or that it was destroyed?

12† In the circuits you have used so far, in a given length of time, how does the charge flowing out of the battery compare with the charge flowing into the battery?

9.6 THE EFFECT OF THE CHARGE METER ON THE CIRCUIT

You have seen that two hydrogen cells connected in series give the same readings: a hydrogen cell does not consume charge. Does this mean that such cells do not affect the circuit at all? Figure 9.9 shows two circuits, each containing a battery and a bulb. One circuit has one hydrogen cell and the other has two hydrogen cells. Both photographs were made after the battery had been connected for 10 minutes. Notice that the water level dropped more in the circuit containing only one cell, indicating that more charge flowed in that circuit than in the other during the same time.

A hydrogen cell does not destroy charge. However, its inclusion in a circuit reduces the quantity of charge that flows through the circuit in a given time. In the example shown in Figure 9.9, the additional cell reduced the volume of hydrogen produced in 10.0 minutes from 24.8 cm^3 to 14.5 cm^3. In other words, the production of hydrogen dropped from $\dfrac{24.8 \text{ cm}^3}{10.0 \text{ min}} = 2.48$ cm^3/min to $\dfrac{14.5 \text{ cm}^3}{10.0 \text{ min}} = 1.45$ cm^3/min when the second hydrogen cell was added to the circuit. We conclude, therefore, that the quantity of charge that flowed through the circuit in 1 minute with two cells was less than it was with one cell.

Such an effect on the behavior of the circuit is a very undesirable feature of the hydrogen cell as a charge meter. In general, we like any measuring instrument to have as small an effect as possible on the system to which it is applied. If this is not so, then as a result of the measurement we have a very different system than before. Suppose, for example, that you wish to measure the pressure of the air inside an inflated bicycle tire. The usual tire pressure gauge

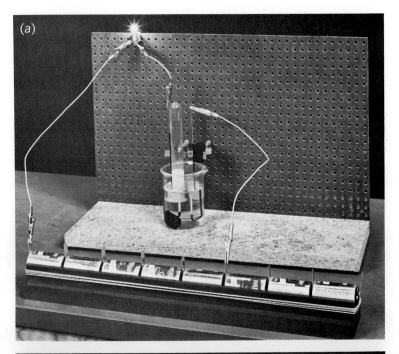

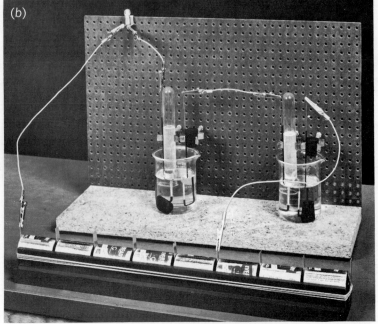

Figure 9.9

(a) One hydrogen cell in series with a light bulb. The circuit had been operating for 10 minutes when the photograph was taken, and 24.8 cm^3 of hydrogen had been produced. (b) With two hydrogen cells in series with the light bulb, only 14.5 cm^3 of hydrogen was produced in 10 minutes. Note that the light bulb is much dimmer than in (a).

allows some air to escape from the tire when the pressure is measured. Consequently the pressure inside the tire is reduced. As long as the gauge removes only a small fraction of the air in the tire, we can disregard the small pressure drop caused by the use of the gauge. However, a pressure gauge that would withdraw a large fraction of the air from the tire would be useless. Similarly, we would like to avoid the use of a charge meter that has such a large effect on the charge flow. It is worthwhile, therefore, to look for other ways to measure the quantity of charge passing through a point in an electric circuit.

A very convenient way to measure charge that eliminates this difficulty is to use a clock and an instrument called an ammeter. An ammeter measures how much charge flows through a circuit per unit time. Figure 9.10 shows the circuit of Figure 9.9 with one and two ammeters instead of hydrogen cells connected in series. Notice that adding a second ammeter changed neither the brightness of the bulb nor the reading of the first ammeter. The additional ammeter had no measurable effect on the circuit.

---

13 Why are the masses of thermometer bulbs always much smaller than the masses of the objects whose temperatures they are made to measure?

14 Suggest an experiment to determine whether adding a light bulb to a series circuit reduces the charge that flows around the circuit in a fixed time interval.

9.7   CHARGE, CURRENT, AND TIME

To see how a clock and an ammeter, which measures the flow of charge per unit of time, can be used to determine the total quantity of charge, first consider the following situations. A worker is paid $5 an hour or, to put it another way, he is paid at the rate of 5 dollars/hour. If he works for 8 hours, his total earnings will be 5 (dollars/hour) × 8 hours = 40 dollars. Similarly, suppose we are told that 3 gallons of water flows into a pool every second and that

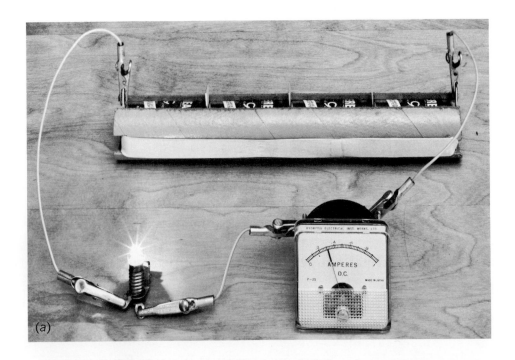

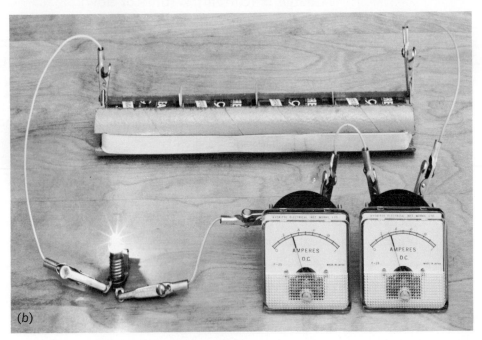

Figure 9.10

(*a*) One ammeter in series with a light bulb. (*b*) Adding another ammeter to the circuit in (*a*) changes neither the brightness of the bulb nor the charge per unit time (measured in amperes on the ammeter scales) flowing through the circuit.

this flow continues for 60 seconds. The amount of water that flows into the pool in 60 seconds is, therefore,

$$3 \text{ (gallons/second)} \times 60 \text{ seconds} = 180 \text{ gallons.}$$

These examples suggest a general relationship:

Total of something = (rate of something) × (time)

We shall use this general relationship to measure the electric charge that passes through a point in a circuit:

Total charge = (rate of flow of charge) × (time)

The rate of flow of electric charge, which is what an ammeter measures, is called the electric current, so

Charge = (current) × (time of flow).

An ammeter measures the current in units called "amperes" (A). The charge when measured by the ammeter and a clock is then expressed in units of amperes × seconds:

Charge (ampere-seconds) = current (amperes) × time (seconds)

Since charge can be measured either with a hydrogen cell or with an ammeter and a clock, there must be a relationship between the quantity of charge measured in ampere-seconds and the quantity of charge measured in cm^3 of hydrogen. This relationship is the subject of the next experiment.

15† How many ampere-seconds of charge flow through an ammeter if it reads (a) 2.0 amperes for 10 seconds? (b) 0.4 amperes for 3.0 minutes? (c) 6.0 amperes for 12.0 seconds?

16 How long must current flow through an ammeter reading 0.75 amperes to have 20 ampere-seconds of charge flow through the meter?

17 You can use an ammeter and a clock to measure charge. How would you use an automobile speedometer and a clock to measure distance?

9.8 EXPERIMENT MEASURING CHARGE WITH AN AMMETER AND A CLOCK

Figure 9.11 shows a hydrogen cell and an ammeter connected in series. To find the relationship between charge measured in ampere-seconds and the charge measured in cm^3 of hydrogen, you can measure the volume of hydrogen and the current at the end of every minute until the graduated cylinder is nearly full of hydrogen. Then you can use your data to make a graph of charge measured in ampere-seconds as a function of charge measured in cm^3 of hydrogen.

Figure 9.11
An ammeter and a hydrogen cell connected in series. A graduated cylinder is used to collect the hydrogen so that the volume of gas can be measured directly. When you connect up this circuit, be sure that the positive terminal of the ammeter is connected to the positive terminal of the battery.

Since the current may change during the experiment, you will have to know the average current. To find it, you can add all the ammeter readings up to and including the time you make a given volume reading and divide by the number of readings. This procedure is valid as long as you have measured the current at equal time intervals.

If you use between six and eight flashlight cells, you can fill the graduated cylinder with hydrogen in a reasonable time.

Use your data to draw a graph of charge expressed in ampere-seconds as a function of charge expressed in cm^3 of hydrogen. Compare your graph with those of your classmates.

- What volume of hydrogen is produced by a flow of 1.0 ampere-seconds of charge?

- Does the volume of hydrogen produced by a flow of 1.0 ampere-seconds of charge depend on the number of flashlight cells used in the circuit?

- Does it depend on the current?

The volume of hydrogen produced by 1.0 ampere-seconds of charge can vary. Both the pressure and the temperature of the gas will affect the result. For example, doing the experiment in Denver, Colorado, on a hot day will give quite different results from what you would get by doing it in Boston, Massachusetts, on a cold day. However, if we calculate the *mass* of hydrogen produced in each case in 1 second, we find it is the same in both places. When one ampere flows through the cell, 1.04×10^{-5} g of hydrogen are produced per second, regardless of the temperature or pressure of the gas.

18† If the ammeter in the circuit of Figure 9.11 measured charge instead of charge per unit time, how would the position of the needle be affected as hydrogen was produced?

19 In doing Experiment 9.8, group I measured the current at the end of every minute during a 5-minute run, and got the following data:

Time (min)	Current (A)
1	0.50
2	0.80
3	0.81
4	0.82
5	0.82

Group II took only two readings of current during the 5-minute run, without paying any attention to the time of the readings, and recorded the following data:

First reading   0.50 A
Second reading   0.82 A

a) What was the charge passing through the circuit during each interval of 1 minute in the experiment of group I?

b) What was the total charge passing through the circuit in the 5-minute run in the experiment of group I?

c) What was the average current during the 5-minute run in the experiment of group I?

d) Can group II answer any of these questions for its experiment?

20 Calculate from the data of Experiment 9.8 how many cubic centimeters of hydrogen gas at room temperature you would collect if you ran a hydrogen cell for 5 minutes with an ammeter reading of 0.5 ampere.

For Home, Desk, and Lab

21 Examine a light bulb at home and see if you can determine where the two contacts are that make the bulb operate.

22 There are no connecting wires in flashlights. Explain how it is possible for any charge to flow.

23 Suppose you have three identical light bulbs, some connecting wire, and a battery. Make a sketch of all the different possible ways to connect the battery and bulbs, using all three bulbs each time. Label which circuits are series circuits and which are parallel circuits.

24 Draw a circuit diagram that includes some identical hydrogen cells, showing how you could collect exactly three times as much hydrogen in one cell as in one of the others during the same time.

25 "Electric charge is neither created nor destroyed when it flows around a circuit." What happens to the electric charge when the circuit is disconnected at one point?

26 Someone suggests that the brightness of a bulb depends on the total quantity of charge that passes through it, and not on the quantity of charge per unit time. How would you disprove this?

27 What would happen if the connections to the battery were interchanged (reversed) in the circuit shown in Figure 9.11?

28 In a laboratory experiment, a student measures the current in a
    circuit as a function of time. What average current flowed through
    the circuit, if Figure D is the graph of current versus time? If Figure
    E is the graph of current versus time?

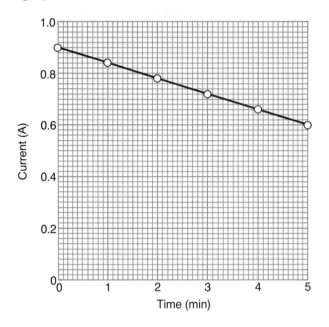

Figure D
For problem 28

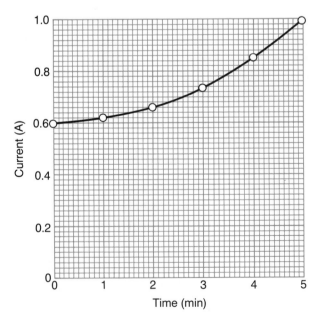

Figure E
For problem 28

29 A hydrogen cell and two ammeters are connected in series. One ammeter reads 0.50 A and the other reads 0.65 A. In 10 minutes 52 cm^3 of hydrogen is produced. Using your graph from Experiment 9.8, decide which ammeter should be set aside for repair.

30 How could you use an ammeter and a hydrogen cell and the graph from Experiment 9.8 as a clock for which each cubic-centimeter mark on the 50-cm^3 graduated cylinder represents one minute?

31 How many seconds would it take to produce one gram of hydrogen in a hydrogen cell through which a current of one ampere flows?

32 Is there any evidence from the experiments you have done so far that suggests in what direction charge flows around a circuit?

Themes for Short Essays

1 Electric charge and temperature are mentioned in section 9.1 as examples of quantities that are measured indirectly. Invent an indirect way of measuring appetite. Describe the procedure in detail. Discuss the assumptions you make and the reliability of the procedure.

2 The effect of a measurement or an observation on what is being measured or observed is not limited to the laboratory. Here are two examples. How can the score of a football game be affected by the watching crowd? Does a highway-patrol officer affect the number of speeding motorists? Use these or other examples to write a brief essay on the effect of measurement on what is being measured.

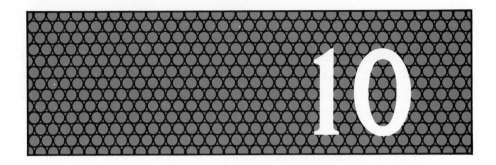

Atoms and Electric Charge

10.1 THE CHARGE PER MOLE OF HYDROGEN AND OXYGEN

In the last chapter we used the amount of hydrogen produced by electrolysis as a measure for the quantity of electric charge that flowed in a circuit. The greater the amount of charge that passed through the cell, the greater the amount of hydrogen and oxygen produced. This indicates a connection between matter and electric charge. To investigate this connection further, we shall study electrolytic cells where the passage of electric charge causes the deposit of other elements on an electrode. Since we believe these elements accumulate on an electrode atom by atom, it will be useful to compare the quantities of charge needed to release the same number of atoms of various elements, specifically a mole of atoms.

In the case of hydrogen, a flow of 1 ampere-second of charge releases 1.04×10^{-5} g of the gas. From section 8.10, you know that the mass of a mole of hydrogen atoms is 1.01 g. Thus, to release a mole of hydrogen atoms, the charge needed is

$$\frac{1.01 \text{ g}}{1.04 \times 10^{-5} \text{ g/ampere-second}} = 97,100 \text{ ampere-seconds.}$$

More careful measurements give a value of 96,500 ampere-seconds.

From the molecular formula for water, H_2O, it follows that the decomposition of one mole of water molecules yields two moles of hydrogen atoms and one mole of oxygen atoms. Since the same quantity of electric charge passes through both electrodes, each mole of oxygen atoms must require twice the charge needed to release one mole of hydrogen atoms. Therefore we conclude that it takes $2 \times 96,500$ ampere-seconds, or 193,000 ampere-seconds, of charge to release one mole of oxygen atoms.

1† **During the electrolysis of water, which collecting tube has the greater number of atoms of gas in it at a given time?**

2 **One ampere-second of charge yields 1.04×10^{-5} g of hydrogen. How many grams of oxygen will 1 ampere-second of charge release? What volume will the oxygen occupy?**

10.2   EXPERIMENT   THE ELECTROPLATING OF ZINC

We have just seen that there is a simple 2-to-1 ratio for the quantities of charge needed to release one mole of oxygen atoms and one mole of hydrogen atoms. We can release elements other than hydrogen and oxygen by electrolysis. How does the charge per mole of atoms compare for different elements?

In this experiment, we shall determine the quantity of charge needed to release one mole of zinc atoms from a solution containing zinc. Since zinc is a solid, it will be deposited on the electrode. We can determine the mass released by massing this electrode before and after we electrolyze the solution. The charge per mole of atoms can then be found from:

$$\text{Charge/mole} = \frac{\text{charge needed to release sample of element}}{\text{number of moles of atoms in sample}}$$

With an ammeter and a clock you can measure the charge in ampere-seconds. From the change in mass of the electrode and the mass of a zinc atom (in u), we can determine how many moles of zinc atoms were plated during the experiment. The mass of a zinc atom in u is given in Table 8.4.

The zinc-plating cell consists of two zinc electrodes and a solution containing zinc. After massing each of the two zinc electrodes, you can connect the zinc-plating cell to the ammeter as shown in Figure 10.1. Do not connect the battery to the ammeter and the plating cell until you are ready to time the run.

Begin by connecting the circuit to only one flashlight cell, but quickly increase the number of cells until you get the largest current for which the ammeter needle is still on the scale.

A run of 20 to 25 minutes will deposit enough zinc to be massed on the balance. Since the current may change during the run, taking a current reading every minute will be useful.

When the run is over, rinse both electrodes by dipping them in a beaker of water. Gently dry the electrodes with paper towels and mass each one on your balance. Compare the change in mass of one electrode with that of the other. Use Table 8.4 to find how many moles of zinc atoms were deposited.

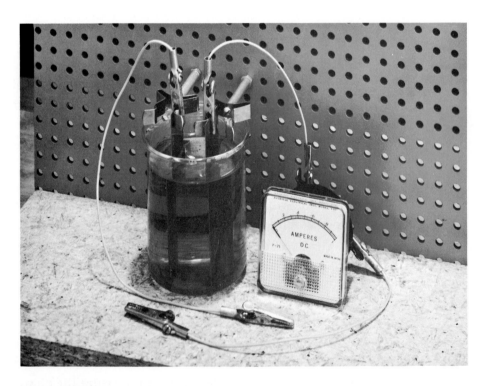

Figure 10.1

A zinc-plating cell and an ammeter connected in series. The wire lead on the right comes from the ammeter terminal marked "+" and is connected to the positive terminal of the battery (not shown in the photograph).

From the average current that flowed through the circuit and the duration of the run, calculate the electric charge in ampere-seconds that was used to plate out the zinc.

- How much charge was needed to deposit one mole of zinc atoms?
- How does this compare with the charge needed to release one mole of hydrogen atoms?

3 A nickel-plating cell was run for 10 minutes at an average current of 0.80 ampere. It was found that 0.15 g of nickel was deposited on one electrode.
a) What is the mass of one mole of nickel atoms? (See Table 8.4.)
b) How many moles of nickel atoms were deposited?
c) What charge flowed in ampere-seconds?
d) What is the charge per mole of nickel atoms in this experiment?

4 In Experiment 10.2: The Electroplating of Zinc, one student calculated the charge in ampere-seconds for each minute, added all his results, and then divided by the total time in minutes. Another student found the average current and multiplied by the time in seconds. Which method is correct for determining the total charge?

5 A nickel-plating cell is run for 5 minutes at a current of 0.6 amperes. Then the battery leads are reversed, and the cell runs 5 minutes more at the same current. What would you expect to have happened at the electrodes? Would the result be the same for a cell electrolyzing water?

10.3 THE FARADAY AND THE ELEMENTARY CHARGE

Hydrogen, oxygen, and zinc are not the only elements which can be collected at the electrodes of an electrolytic cell. Other elements can also be collected this way and the charge needed to deposit one mole of atoms can be determined. However, the procedure may in some cases be considerably more difficult than the ones you have used. For example, sodium cannot be plated out from a solution of sodium chloride in water. Hydrogen will be produced at the negative electrode, and the sodium will remain in the solution. Chlorine will bubble up at the other electrode, but since chlorine is quite soluble in water, the amount of chlorine collected as gas in the test tube is much less than the amount of chlorine actually produced. To obtain reliable data from which to calculate the charge per mole of sodium and chlorine atoms, one has to pass a current through molten sodium chloride and prevent any contact of the sodium with water vapor or oxygen. Potassium requires a similar treatment.

Despite the technical complications, many elements have been produced by electrolysis, and the charge required per mole has been determined. Table 10.1 shows the ratios of the charge per mole for some common elements to the charge per mole of hydrogen atoms, as obtained from experiments more precise than those you have done.

There is a simple relationship between the charge per mole of atoms of an element and the charge per atom of the same element:

Charge/mole = (number of atoms in a mole) × (charge/atom)

Thus, the ratio of the charge per mole for any two elements equals the ratio of the charge per single atom of the same element because the number of atoms in a mole will cancel out. In particular,

$$\frac{\text{charge/mole of atoms of element}}{\text{charge/mole of atoms of hydrogen}} = \frac{\text{charge/atom of element}}{\text{charge/atom of hydrogen}}$$

For example, from Table 10.1, the charge per atom of aluminum is three times the charge per atom of hydrogen. However, since we do not yet know the number of atoms in a mole, we do not yet know what the charge per atom is in ampere-seconds.* Nevertheless, Table 10.1 strongly suggests that the electric charge needed to produce one atom of hydrogen by electrolysis has a fundamental significance. It is the smallest quantity of charge that is involved in the electrolysis of any material. But, more than that, the charge required to deposit one atom of any element is equal to the charge per atom of hydrogen or to a small whole number times this charge. There is no element that requires, say, 2.5 times this charge to release one atom. For these reasons, the charge needed to release one hydrogen atom is known as the elementary charge. It is the smallest quantity of charge now known to occur in nature.

About 150 years ago Michael Faraday in England carried out electrolysis experiments similar to the ones you have done. He found

*One method of finding the number of atoms in a mole is described in Chapter 11.

Table 10.1

Element	Symbol	Charge per mole of atoms of element / Charge per mole of hydrogen atoms
Aluminum	Al	3.00
Bromine	Br	1.00
Calcium	Ca	2.00
Chlorine	Cl	1.00
Chromium	Cr	6.00
Iodine	I	1.00
Lead	Pb	2.00
Magnesium	Mg	2.00
Mercury	Hg	2.00
Nickel	Ni	2.00
Oxygen	O	2.00
Potassium	K	1.00
Silver	Ag	1.00
Sodium	Na	1.00

that the mass of an element deposited on an electrode is proportional to the quantity of charge that flows through the circuit. But Faraday, who was not convinced that matter was composed of atoms, did not suggest an elementary unit of charge. The charge needed to release one mole of hydrogen atoms (96,500 ampere-seconds) is called a "faraday," in his honor.

The first to propose the idea of an elementary charge was Hermann Helmholtz in Germany. In 1881 he related the results of Faraday's experiments to the atomic theory with this bold declaration: "If we accept the hypothesis that the elementary substances are composed of atoms we cannot avoid the conclusion that electricity also . . . is divided into definite elementary portions, which behave like atoms of electricity."

So far, we have seen that the units we use to measure physical quantities are quite arbitrary: the centimeter is as good a unit of length as the inch. Nowhere have we seen any preference in nature for one unit over another. The electric charge is different. Nature provides us with its own fundamental unit, the elementary charge.

6 A hydrogen cell is connected in series with a silver-plating cell.
  a) How many atoms of hydrogen will be produced for every atom of silver deposited?
  b) How many grams of hydrogen will be produced for every gram of silver deposited?

7 Will an electric current which passes through a sodium-plating and a lead-plating cell in series ever deposit the same mass of metal in each cell? (See Tables 8.4 and 10.1.)

8 What is the significance of recording the ratios in Table 10.1 as 3.00, 1.00, 2.00, . . . , and not simply as 3, 1, 2, . . . ?

10.4 THE ELEMENTARY CHARGE AND THE LAW OF CONSTANT PROPORTIONS

Consider two elements A and B which combine to form a compound. If A and B require equal numbers of elementary charges per atom in electrolysis, then they combine according to the formula AB, that is, one atom of A for every atom of B. On the basis of this generalization, we would predict from Table 10.1 that hydrogen and iodine combine according to the formula HI, and that mercury and oxygen form the oxide HgO. When these compounds are analyzed, this is indeed found to be their composition.

If element A requires one elementary charge per atom and element B requires two, then if they combine at all they will do so according to the formula A_2B (or BA_2), since each time two elementary charges release one atom of B, two atoms of A are released. The compounds H_2O, Na_2O, and $MgCl_2$ are examples of this kind of composition.

Accurate measurements of the mass ratios of the elements in these and many other compounds confirm predictions based on Table 10.1. Additional examples are given in Table 10.2.

Table 10.2

Element	Elementary charge per atom	Element	Elementary charge per atom	Simplest formula of compound
Iron	2	Chlorine	1	$FeCl_2$
Silver	1	Chlorine	1	$AgCl$
Hydrogen	1	Bromine	1	HBr
Lithium	1	Oxygen	2	Li_2O
Silver	1	Oxygen	2	Ag_2O

To sum up, once we have found the number of elementary charges per atom for various elements by electrolysis, we know how many atoms of one element would combine with one atom of another element. This is so even for compounds that cannot be electrolyzed. The number of elementary charges per atom and the atomic mass fix the proportions in the law of constant proportions. When we first encountered this law, we had no way of relating mass ratios to anything else. Now we see that they are closely connected to atomic masses and the number of elementary charges per atom.

But two elements can sometimes form more than one compound. Does this mean that the same element can have different charges per atom in different compounds? We shall try to answer this question in the next experiment.

9 One can write the simplest formula for water either from the data on the combining masses and atomic masses of hydrogen and oxygen, or from the data on the charge per atom for these two elements in electrolysis. Upon what conservation laws are these arguments based?

10 Using Table 10.1, write the simplest formulas for (a) magnesium oxide, (b) chromium oxide, (c) aluminum oxide.

11† Element A combines with element B according to the simplest formula A_2B. Element B has been found to require two elementary charges per atom in electrolysis. If element A could be plated out in electrolysis, how many elementary charges per atom would it require?

12 In the synthesis of zinc chloride (Experiment 6.4) you showed that the ratio of zinc reacted to product formed was 0.48. Using the data from Tables 8.4 and 10.1, what ratio do you obtain?

10.5   EXPERIMENT   TWO COMPOUNDS OF COPPER

The two compounds of copper to be investigated are copper sulfate (a blue solution) and copper chloride (an almost colorless solution).

Mass two copper electrodes after marking them with identifying letters and your initials.

Connect two copper-plating cells, each with copper electrodes, in series with an ammeter as shown in Figure 10.2. In each cell the negative electrode is the one you have marked for identification. Add the blue solution to one cell and the almost colorless solution to the other.

Figure 10.2
Two copper-plating cells connected in series. The wire lead on the right runs from the ammeter terminal marked "+" to the positive terminal of the battery (not shown). Note which electrodes are labeled for identification. The cell on the left contains the dark-blue solution, and the one on the right contains the almost colorless solution.

Using the same procedure as in Experiment 10.2, adjust the current close to 1 amp in order to deposit in 15 minutes enough copper to mass. Be sure you record the current every minute during the run.

After the marked electrodes have been carefully rinsed and dried, you can mass them and find the gain in mass of each.

- How many moles of atoms of copper were deposited in each electrolytic cell by the charge that flowed through the circuit?

- Without further calculation, what can you say about the quantity of charge required to plate out one mole of copper atoms from the blue solution, compared with the charge needed to plate out one mole of copper atoms from the colorless solution?

- From the average current that flowed through the circuit and the duration of the run, what is the number of faradays needed to plate out a mole of copper atoms from each of the two solutions?

There are two oxides of copper—that is, two compounds containing only copper and oxygen.

- On the basis of the results of this experiment, what do you predict are their simplest formulas?

13† If in the experiment described above, the electrodes in one of the cells were bent so that they were touching throughout the run, what effect would this have on the results?

14 In Experiment 8.7 you found that twice as much chlorine combined with a given mass of copper in one chloride of copper as in another. What could be the simplest formulas for these substances, on the basis of that experiment alone? What limitations are placed on these choices by Experiment 10.5 and Table 10.1?

10.6 A NEW LOOK AT THE LAW OF MULTIPLE PROPORTIONS

When we first introduced the atomic model of matter in Chapter 8, we made the following prediction: If two elements form more than one compound, the ratio of the masses of one element that combine with a fixed mass of the other is given by a ratio of small whole numbers. You checked this prediction in Experiment 8.7 with two compounds of copper and chlorine. For a fixed amount of copper the ratio of the masses of chlorine in the two compounds was 2:1. You had no way of predicting what those small whole numbers might be. Now you are in a better position. With the results of the last experiment you can tell what the numbers would be for copper compounds.

There are other elements besides copper which require different numbers of elementary charges per atom to release them, depending on the compound from which they are plated out. Table 10.3 lists some of them, including a few which have appeared already in Table 10.1.

We can now use the reasoning we employed in section 10.4 to predict the simplest formulas for different compounds containing these elements. Some examples are shown in Table 10.4.

Table 10.3

Element	Symbol	Number of elementary charges per atom for different compounds
Chromium	Cr	2, 3, 6
Iron	Fe	2, 3
Mercury	Hg	1, 2
Tin	Sn	2, 4

Table 10.4

Element	Elementary charge per atom	Element	Elementary charge per atom	Simplest formula of compound
Iron	2	Oxygen	2	FeO
Iron	3	Oxygen	2	Fe_2O_3
Tin	2	Chlorine	1	$SnCl_2$
Tin	4	Chlorine	1	$SnCl_4$
Chromium	2	Oxygen	2	CrO
Chromium	3	Oxygen	2	Cr_2O_3
Chromium	6	Oxygen	2	CrO_3

15 There are two compounds containing only chlorine and mercury. What would you predict as the simplest formula for these two compounds?

16 Using the data in Table 10.3, write the simplest formula for the two oxides of mercury.

17 Which of the following simplest formulas do you think describe real compounds? (See Tables 10.1 and 10.3.)
    (a) SnH_3 (b) $NaCl_2$ (c) SnO_2

10.7 THE MOTION OF ELECTRIC CHARGE THROUGH A VACUUM

So far we have been concerned with the flow of charge in electrolytic cells. In these cells the motion of charge is related to the motion of atoms.

You know that electric charge moves freely in the electric wiring of buildings and in the connecting wires of your laboratory apparatus. Can this flow of charge through solid wires be related to the motion of atoms? It hardly seems possible. In contrast to gases and liquids, solids keep their shape. This means that the atoms of a solid are not free to move about.

To get some idea of what may carry charges in a metal, we shall first describe and analyze an experiment in which charge flows through a vacuum. Figure 10.3(a) shows a vacuum tube of a kind once used in radios and television sets. Nearly all the air (about 99.99999 percent) has been removed from the tube. Figure 10.3(b)

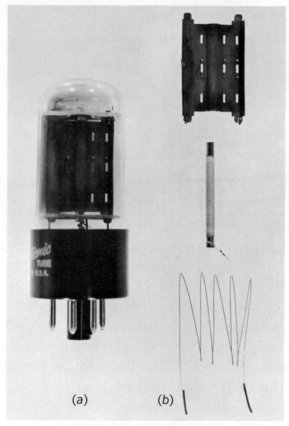

(a)   (b)

Figure 10.3
(a) A general view of a vacuum tube. (b) Separate views of the heater, cathode, and plate.

shows the inside of the tube. The two most important parts are the large rectangular electrode commonly called the "plate," or "anode," and the long, narrow cylindrical electrode called the "cathode." The long zigzag wire is an electric heater that is folded up inside the cathode and insulated from it as shown in Figure 10.4. When sup-

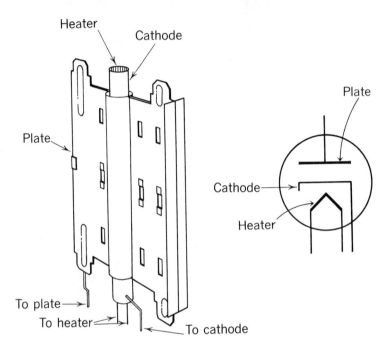

Figure 10.4
The construction of the vacuum tube shown in Figure 10.3, and its schematic representation.

plied with current, the heater and the surrounding cathode get red hot. With the heater connected to an 8-cell battery, we examine the current through the vacuum tube under two conditions. First, the cathode of the tube is connected to the negative end of a 12-cell battery, and the plate is connected through an ammeter to the positive end. There is a current of 0.15 amperes (Figure 10.5). When the cathode is connected to the positive terminal of the 12-cell battery, there is no current (Figure 10.6). Without the heater, there is no current for either connection.

We can summarize the behavior of the vacuum tube in the following way. When the cathode is cold, there is no current. When the cathode is heated, there is current only if it is connected to the negative terminal of the battery.

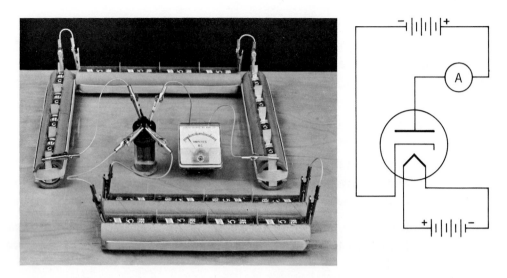

Figure 10.5
Photograph and schematic drawing of the vacuum-tube circuit. The
cathode is heated, and it leads to the negative terminal of the battery.

Does this tell us anything about the direction of motion of the
charge in the tube? Does the heating of the cathode enable it to
receive charges coming from the plate or to emit charges, which then
move to the plate? To help choose between these two possibilities,
think of the evaporation of water near the freezing and boiling
points. Near freezing, the molecules move relatively slowly in the

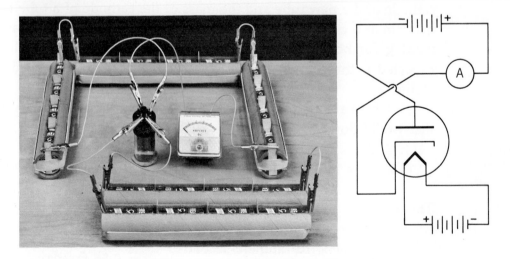

Figure 10.6
The same circuit as in Figure 10.5, except that the cathode is connected
to the positive terminal of the battery (through the ammeter).

liquid and only a few escape per unit of time. At higher temperatures, near boiling, the motion becomes more vigorous and molecules leave the surface of the liquid at a high rate.

This analogy suggests that charges escape from the hot cathode and move to the anode. Does this mean that some of the atoms that make up the cathode actually carry the charge to the plate?

18† A vacuum tube has terminals that connect to the cathode, the plate, and the two ends of the heater. If you find which two go to the heater, how can you find out which terminal connects to the plate?

19 If the plate, instead of the cathode, is heated in the cases illustrated in Figures 10.5 and 10.6, what result would you expect to observe in each case?

10.8 ELECTRONS

We can answer the question at the end of the preceding section by massing the cathode of a vacuum tube before it is assembled and again after it has been in use for some time. But we do not even have to do that. Vacuum tubes were mass-produced, so that the mass of the cathode is nearly constant for all tubes of a given type. It will be enough, therefore, to compare the mass of the cathode of a new tube with that of a used tube. We did that and found that the mass of the cathode of the new tube and the mass of the cathode of a tube that had run at a current of 0.15 ampere for 100 hours were the same: 0.224 g for both cases. What decrease in mass should we have expected if the charge flowing through the tube were carried by atoms?

There are 3.6×10^5 seconds in 100 hours, so the total charge that would flow would be

$$0.15 \text{ ampere} \times 3.6 \times 10^5 \text{ seconds} = 5.4 \times 10^4 \text{ ampere-seconds.}$$

This is

$$\frac{5.4 \times 10^4 \text{ ampere-seconds}}{9.65 \times 10^4 \text{ ampere-seconds/faraday}} = 0.56 \text{ faraday.}$$

Now, to know how much mass is associated with this number of faradays, we must know what kind of atoms make up the surface of the cathode. Actually, the cathode surface is composed of a mixture of several oxides; a hot surface composed of this mixture has been found to be a better emitter of charges than a pure-metal surface. The lightest of the atoms in these oxides are the oxygen atoms. So, for simplicity, we shall assume that oxygen atoms carry all the charge that flows.

We shall further assume that one oxygen atom carries two elementary charges, the same charge that is required to release an oxygen atom in the electrolysis of water. Under this assumption it will take 2.0 faradays to release one mole of oxygen atoms from the surface of the cathode (Table 10.1). Thus,

$$\frac{0.56 \text{ faraday}}{2.0 \text{ faradays/mole}} = 0.28 \text{ mole of oxygen atoms}$$

would leave the cathode in 100 hours. This is 4.5 g of oxygen. But the entire mass of the cathode is less than 0.25 g!

The conclusion is inescapable: the charge is not carried across the vacuum tube by atoms. There must be carriers of a different kind which, from our observations, have the following properties:

a) They come off a hot cathode connected to the negative end of a battery but not from a hot cathode connected to the positive end.

b) They do not seem to reduce the mass of the cathode.

These carriers are called "electrons." Since they move from the cathode, which is connected to the negative end of the battery, they are said to be "negatively charged."

---

20   Use Table 8.4 to verify that 0.28 mole of oxygen atoms has a mass of 4.5 g.

21   Suppose the cathode of a vacuum tube were made of copper. What would be the loss in mass after 100 hours at 0.15 ampere if copper atoms carried the charge across the tube?

22 The mass of an electron is about $\dfrac{1}{2,000}$ of the mass of a hydrogen atom. How long would you have to run the vacuum tube described in section 10.8 in order to show that electrons do not accumulate on the plate, increasing its mass at the expense of the cathode?

10.9 ATOMS AND IONS: AN EXTENSION OF THE ATOMIC MODEL

Very early in our study of electricity we adopted the eighteenth-century idea that when an electrical device is operating, something is moving through it. We called that something the electric charge and developed ways of measuring it (section 9.1). Now we are in a position to develop this idea into a more concrete model. In so doing we shall also bring the model up to date.

The first thing the model must accomplish is to tie together the motion of charge when it is accompanied by the motion of atoms and its motion when it is not. To have a definite situation in mind, consider a circuit consisting of a battery, a copper-plating cell, and a vacuum tube (Figure 10.7). You know from your experience that in the copper cell, copper dissolves at the electrode leading to the positive terminal of the battery and plates out on the electrode leading to the negative terminal. We say that charge carriers that move away from the positive terminal of a battery are "positively charged." On the other hand, in the vacuum tube the charge carriers

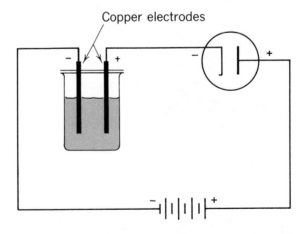

Figure 10.7
A circuit consisting of a battery, a vacuum tube, and a copper-plating cell. The heating circuit for the cathode is not shown.

are electrons, which move away from the cathode when it leads to the negative terminal of the battery and are negatively charged.

The problem now facing us is: how can electrons and atoms be related to account for the overall motion of charge in the circuit? This question was answered satisfactorily only in the twentieth century; and although the resulting model was based on a variety of experiments, the passage of charge through cells, metal wires, and vacuum tubes provides the main clues.

The basic features of the extended atomic model are as follows: An atom is made up of a part which is positively charged and a number of negatively charged electrons. The total charge on an isolated atom is normally zero; the atom as a whole is electrically neutral. If an atom loses an electron, it becomes positively charged. On the other hand, if an atom gains an electron, it becomes negatively charged. Charged atoms are called "ions."

For example, when a neutral sodium atom loses an electron, it becomes a positive sodium ion. This is expressed in symbols as:

$$Na \longrightarrow Na^+ + e^-$$

Similarly, when a neutral chlorine atom gains an electron, it becomes a negative chlorine ion:

$$Cl + e^- \longrightarrow Cl^-$$

Copper and zinc atoms carry two elementary charges in a solution. Thus each of them must give up two electrons to become a doubly charged ion:

$$Cu \longrightarrow Cu^{++} + 2e^-$$
$$Zn \longrightarrow Zn^{++} + 2e^-$$

We shall assume that in a solution which conducts electricity the solute is in ionic form. For example, a solution of copper chloride, $CuCl_2$, conducts electricity. We can look upon the formation of the ions as the combination of the two steps

$$Cu \longrightarrow Cu^{++} + 2e^-$$
and
$$2Cl + 2e^- \longrightarrow 2Cl^-$$

occurring together. The net result is

$$CuCl_2 \longrightarrow Cu^{++} + 2Cl^-$$

"2Cl⁻" means two separate chlorine ions, whereas the subscript 2 in $CuCl_2$ means that in this chloride of copper there are two chlorine atoms for every copper atom.

When copper sulfate, $CuSO_4$, is dissolved in water, the copper atoms separate from the sulfur and oxygen atoms as Cu^{++} ions. The negative ions, called sulfate ions, are each made up of one sulfur atom and four oxygen atoms tightly bound together. We do not know how the charges are distributed among the sulfur atom and the four oxygen atoms; therefore we shall simply write SO_4^{--} for the sulfate ion to indicate that two electrons are attached to the sulfate. When an electric current passes through the copper-plating cell in Figure 10.7, copper from the positive electrode enters the solution as Cu^{++} ions, and copper from the solution plates out on the negative electrode as neutral copper atoms. In terms of ions and electrons this suggests the following reactions:

$$\text{At the positive electrode, } Cu \longrightarrow Cu^{++} + 2e^-$$
$$\text{At the negative electrode, } Cu^{++} + 2e^- \longrightarrow Cu$$

In the copper-plating cell in Figure 10.7, positive copper ions carry charge through the solution. How is charge carried through the metal wires? From the reaction $Cu \longrightarrow Cu^{++} + 2e^-$ at the positive electrode it follows that electrons are moving away from this electrode. By the same reasoning we conclude from the reaction $Cu^{++} + 2e^- \longrightarrow Cu$ at the negative electrode that electrons move from the wire to the electrode. To complete the model we must assume that the electrons can move through metals while ions cannot.

---

23 A copper-plating cell and a vacuum tube were connected in series with a battery. When the heater of the tube was connected, charge moved through the circuit. Do the copper ions in the cell move away from the same battery terminal as the electrons in the tube?

24 What is the number of elementary charges carried by an electron? Base your answer on your plating experiments and the ion-electron model of the atom.

For Home, Desk, and Lab

25 How much charge in ampere-seconds must pass through a hydrogen cell to produce a test tube of hydrogen (about 35 cm^3)? Use the class results for Experiment 9.8.

26 In the electrolysis of water we concluded that water must be continually added to the cell if the same water level is to be maintained in the cell. From your observations of metal-plating cells, do you think that the solutions involved must be replenished if the same liquid level is to be maintained?

27 A student ran a zinc-plating experiment with a battery that was known to contain cells that were weak from constant use. How would this affect his calculations of charge per mole of zinc atoms?

28 Three electrolytic cells were connected in series. Hydrogen was collected in a test tube, and silver and lead were plated out. If 1.01 g of hydrogen is collected, what would be the mass of the elements plated out?

29 The decomposition of uranium chloride yields UCl_4 as the simplest formula for the compound. How many elementary charges per atom do you expect to find in plating uranium out of a solution?

30 Some of the first precise determinations of the atomic masses of many elements were made by the use of plating cells. Suppose a gold-plating cell and a silver-plating cell are connected in series to a battery. When 1.00 g of silver is deposited, 1.83 g of gold is plated out in the gold cell. Knowing that the mass of a silver atom is 108 amu and that one elementary charge is needed to deposit one silver atom, determine the mass of a gold atom in u. What important assumption did you make? How does your value for the mass of a gold atom compare with that in Table 8.4?

31 Element A combines with element B according to the simplest formula A_2B. Element B combines with element C in the simplest formula CB. What might be the simplest formula for a compound made from A and C?

32 A hydrogen-oxygen cell and a copper-plating cell containing the blue solution copper sulfate are connected in series until 10 cm^3 of hydrogen is collected. Write down in words the steps which you

would take to calculate how much copper was plated during this time.

33   Suppose you have a cell consisting of two copper plates and a solution of sulfuric acid. What do you predict will happen if you pass a current through this cell for some time?

34   A student using the evidence present so far in the course proposed that ions form only when water is present. Does the evidence presented in section 7.2 support her argument?

 Theme for a Short Essay

Vacuum tubes were invented early in this century. They played a crucial role in the development of the radio and, later, computers. Today they are hardly used anymore, having been replaced by transistors and integrated circuits. Other inventions, such as the steam locomotive and the seaplane, also have played an important role in the development of technology only to be replaced by newer inventions. Read about an invention of your choice and write a paper titled "The Rise and Fall of . . ."

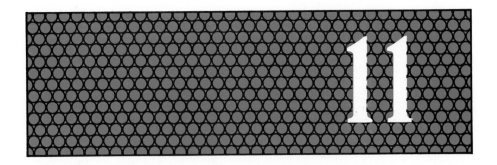

Sizes and Masses of Atoms and Molecules

The atomic model of matter has already proven itself to be very powerful. Yet we know very little about the atoms themselves except their relative masses (Table 8.4). That is, taking the mass of a carbon atom as 12 unified atomic mass units, we know the masses of other atoms. But how many unified atomic mass units are in one gram? Or, a related question, how many atoms are in a mole of atoms? In this chapter we shall answer both questions. As a first step you will find the number of molecules in a tiny droplet of an oily liquid called oleic acid. The method that you will use is explained in the first section.

11.1 THE THICKNESS OF A THIN LAYER

Consider a sample of matter in the form of a rectangular solid. Its volume V is its length times its width times its height, or $V = lwh$ [Figure 11.1(a)]. Since lw is the area of the base, we can say that the volume equals the area of the base times the height. Figure 11.1(b) shows the same sample of matter as that in Figure 11.1(a), with the

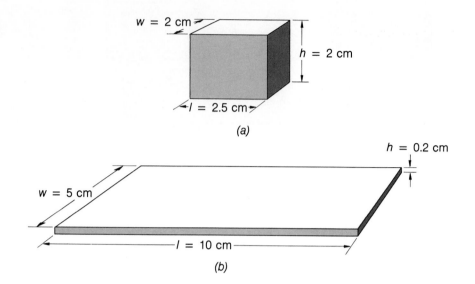

Figure 11.1
The piece of matter in (a) has a volume of $lwh = 2.5$ cm $\times$ 2.0 cm $\times$ 2.0 cm $= 10$ cm³. The flat piece of matter in (b) has the same volume as the matter in (a). The volume of the thin slab in (b) is $lwh = 10$ cm $\times$ 5 cm $\times$ 0.2 cm $= 10$ cm³.

same volume, but now with a rectangular shape that has a larger base and a much smaller height. The material has merely been formed into a different shape. Its volume is still the area of its base times its height. The material might be spread out into an even thinner layer. Its volume would still be equal to the area of its base times its height, and would be unchanged.

Now suppose we have a thin rectangular sheet of some material—a metal foil, for example—whose volume we know. From measurements of its length and width, we can calculate the area of its base. To find the thickness, we divide the known volume by the area of the base.

1 How do you know that there are more than 200 molecules in a spoonful of water?

2† A cube has an edge of length 2 × 10⁻⁷ cm. What is its volume?

11.2 EXPERIMENT THE THICKNESS
OF A THIN SHEET OF METAL

Find the thickness of a rectangular sheet of aluminum foil from its length, width, and volume. You can find the volume from the mass of the sheet and the density of the material (2.7 g/cm³).

- From your calculation of the foil's thickness, how thick can the atoms of aluminum be?

- How thin can they be?

_____

Metals do not flatten out into thin layers by themselves; they have to be rolled or hammered. Hammering, however, is a crude process. Even the most skilled goldsmith, making thin gold leaf for lettering on store windows, must stop when the gold leaf is about 10^{-5} cm thick. In such cases, the minimum thickness is not determined by the size of the fundamental particles of gold but by the difficulty of handling such a thin sheet.

Liquids, on the other hand, tend to spread out into thin layers by themselves. If we pour water on the floor, it spreads out quickly to form a thin layer. We can calculate the thickness of this layer if we know the volume of the water we pour out and the area it covers.

_____

3† In a small-boat harbor, a careless sailor dumps overboard a quart (about 1,000 cm³) of diesel oil. If we assume that this will spread out evenly over the surface of the water to a thickness of 10^{-4} cm, what area will be covered with oil?

4 Spherical lead shot are poured into a square tray 10 cm on a side until they completely cover the bottom. The shot are poured from the tray into a graduated cylinder, which they fill to the 20-cm³ mark.
a) What is the diameter of a single shot?
b) How many shot were in the tray?
c) If the 20 cm³ of shot had a mass of 130 g, what would be the mass of a single shot?

5† A tiny drop of mercury has a volume of 1.0×10^{-3} cm³. The density of mercury is about 14 g/cm³. What is the mass of the drop?

6 A goldsmith takes 19.3 g of gold and hammers it until he has a thin sheet of foil 100 cm in length and 100 cm in width. The density of gold is 19.3 g/cm^3.

a) What is the volume of gold?
b) What is the area of the gold sheet?
c) What is the thickness of the gold sheet?

11.3 EXPERIMENT THE SIZE AND MASS OF AN OLEIC ACID MOLECULE

Under proper conditions, oil and certain other substances can spread out even more thinly than water. Since oil does not dissolve in water but floats on top of it, we often see it spread out on a water surface in a thin, rainbow-colored film. Oleic acid, a compound of hydrogen, carbon, and oxygen, does not dissolve in water but spreads out into an even thinner layer than oil does. In fact, a single drop of this liquid of the size obtained from a medicine dropper will spread so thin as to cover the entire surface of a small wading pool.

To measure the thinnest layer that this substance will form on a small surface of water, we must have a measurable volume of oleic acid that is much smaller than a drop from a medicine dropper. The volume of such a tiny quantity divided by the area of the layer it forms equals the thickness of the layer.*

Pour tap water into a tray to a depth of about one centimeter, and allow it to stand for about 5 minutes so that all movement of the water has stopped. Then sprinkle on the water just enough fine powder to make the powder barely visible. When a tiny amount of oleic acid is dropped onto the water surface, the powder will be pushed aside, allowing us to see the oleic acid film when it spreads out across the water.

Bend a piece of fine wire into a narrow V and clean it with alcohol. When it is dry, dip the tip of the V into oleic acid until a very small droplet clings to the inside of the V. Take care not to immerse it more than is necessary to obtain one small droplet.

---

* The volume of a thin cylinder or disk, like that of a rectangular sheet, is equal to the area of the base times the height, no matter how short the cylinder. In the case of a cylinder, however, the base is a circle and its area is equal to πr^2, where r is the radius of the base.

To get a rough idea of the volume of the droplet it will suffice to assume that the droplet is a cube and to estimate the length of its side. To do that, you use a centimeter scale and a magnifying glass.

- What is the volume of the droplet?

Dip the wire tip into the water several times, until the oleic acid layer stops expanding (Figure 11.2).

(a)

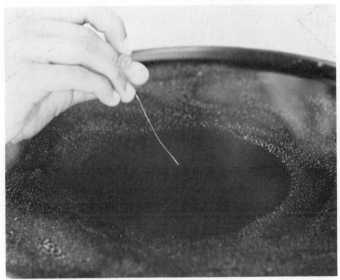

(b)

Figure 11.2
(a) Dipping the wire tip into the water which has been sprinkled lightly with a fine powder.
(b) A close-up of the resulting circle.

- What is the diameter of the circular area covered by the film that is formed?

- If the film forms only a rough circle, how would you find the area?

- From your volume and area estimates, what is the thickness of the layer?

In your calculation of this fantastically small thickness, you used only the fact that the height of a cylinder equals its volume divided by the area of its base. To draw any conclusions about the size of oleic acid molecules from the thickness of the layer, we have to make the following assumption: The oleic acid spreads out until the layer is only one molecule thick. From this assumption, it follows that the thickness you calculated is the height of a single molecule.

So far we have found only the height of a molecule of oleic acid. Other experiments show that oleic acid molecules are long and thin, with a height about 10 times the width of their base. They stand nearly upright on a water surface when they form a thin layer. Thus we can imagine that a tiny piece of a layer of oleic acid, one molecule thick, looks roughly like the collection of tiny rods seen in Figure 11.3. The area of the base of each rod is then equal to the width of the base squared, as shown in Figure 11.4.

Suppose that all the molecules "touch" one another, as in Figure 11.3. Then, total area of layer = (number of molecules) × (area of base of one molecule), or

$$\text{Number of molecules} = \frac{\text{total area of layer}}{\text{area of base of one molecule}}.$$

- From your data for the height of one molecule and the information that the width is $\frac{1}{10}$ of the height, what is the area of the base of one molecule?

- What is the number of molecules in the layer?

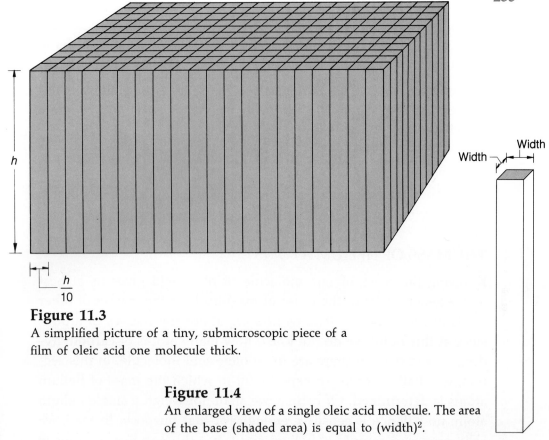

Figure 11.3
A simplified picture of a tiny, submicroscopic piece of a
film of oleic acid one molecule thick.

Figure 11.4
An enlarged view of a single oleic acid molecule. The area
of the base (shaded area) is equal to (width)^2.

- What does this tell you about the number of molecules in
  the droplet you started with?

From the volume of the droplet and the density of oleic acid,
you can calculate the mass of the droplet. The density of oleic acid
is about 1 g/cm^3.

- What was the mass of the droplet of oleic acid?

Knowing the number of molecules in the droplet, you can
now use the relation

$$\text{Mass of one molecule} = \frac{\text{mass of sample}}{\text{number of molecules in sample}}$$

to find the mass of a single molecule of oleic acid.

- What is the mass of one molecule of oleic acid?

7   If 3×10^{-5} cm³ of pure oleic acid forms an oil film with an area of 150 cm², how thick is the film?

8† How many oleic acid molecules occupy 1 cm³ if the volume of one oleic acid molecule is 10^{-23} cm³? Assume that there is no empty space between the molecules.

11.4   THE MASS OF HELIUM ATOMS

Knowing the mass of one molecule of oleic acid gives us at best only a general idea of the order of magnitude of the masses of other kinds of molecules. It tells us nothing about the masses of atoms, since at this point we do not know how many atoms of carbon, hydrogen, and oxygen there are in an oleic acid molecule. In this section, we shall describe an experiment in which the mass of helium atoms is determined. Of course, we shall not weigh a single helium atom: no balance is sensitive enough for that purpose. Instead, we shall prepare a sample of helium and count the number of atoms in it, determine the mass of the sample, and then calculate the mass of a single atom by division:

$$\text{Mass of one atom} = \frac{\text{mass of sample}}{\text{number of atoms in sample}}.$$

We have chosen to find the mass of helium atoms because helium is formed in the decay of several radioactive elements and the atoms can be counted one by one with a radiation counter. Polonium, for example, is a radioactive element that decays only into lead and helium. The last two are stable elements and do not decay further. Suppose we assume that each count from a radioactive sample of polonium signals the decay of one polonium atom and the formation of one lead atom and one helium atom. The clicks of the counter will thus give us the number of helium atoms produced. In practice, we do not have to count all the time. If the rate of decay does not change much, we have only to measure the number of counts per minute and multiply that number by the number of minutes during which the helium has been collected.

We shall now describe an experiment that was performed in 1965 at the Mound Laboratory of the Monsanto Research Corporation using the method we have just outlined.

A small amount of pure polonium was placed inside a quartz tube of known diameter. The air was pumped out, and the tube was then sealed (Figure 11.5). A few days later, enough helium had formed in the tube to allow it to be identified by its spectrum (Figure 11.6).

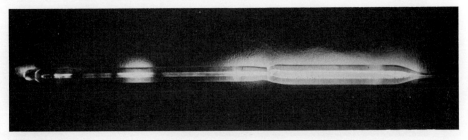

Figure 11.5
The sealed quartz tube containing polonium. The polonium produces a blue glow, caused by the emitted helium particles when they strike the quartz. This photograph was taken in the light from the blue glow.

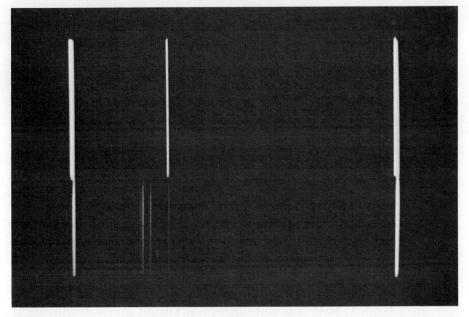

Figure 11.6
The upper half of this photograph is the spectrum of pure helium from a tank of the gas. The lower half is the spectrum of the gas emitted by the polonium in the sealed quartz tube. The two faint lines close together in the lower half are caused by polonium.

After about three weeks, the seal of the tube was broken under water. The water rushed into the tube until it compressed the helium to atmospheric pressure (Figure 11.7). From the volume of the helium and its known density at atmospheric pressure, the mass of the helium was calculated.

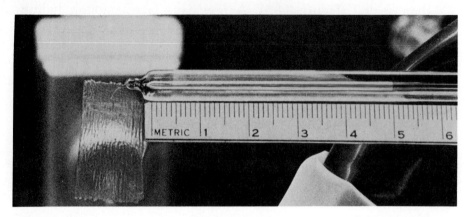

Figure 11.7
The quartz tube containing helium after being opened under water.
The length of the gas column is 5.0 cm.

In principle, the polonium could now be removed from the tube and placed in a counter in order to find the number of disintegrations per minute. However, in practice, this is not possible. A sample large enough to produce a measurable amount of helium in three weeks would give off too many helium particles per second for the counter to count. Therefore, the polonium was first dissolved completely in a large quantity of nitric acid. The solution was further diluted with water. In both steps, the solution was thoroughly mixed to make sure the polonium was evenly distributed throughout. Finally, a tiny drop of the solution was put on a little plate, the acid was evaporated, and the plate placed in a counter (Figure 11.8).

Here is the record of the data of the experiment:

Production of Helium

On March 3, 1965, the polonium was sealed in the evacuated quartz tube. When the seal was broken on March 24, the water rose in the tube and the helium was compressed to a length of 5.0 cm in the tube.

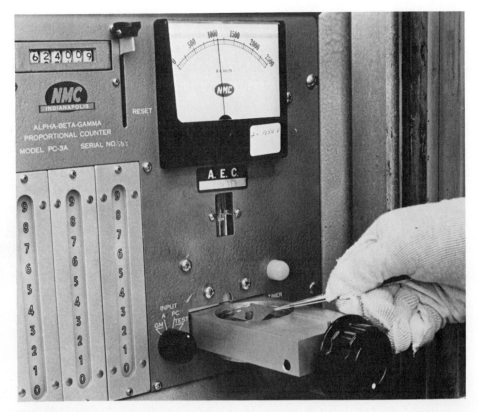

Figure 11.8
A metal plate containing polonium being removed from a radiation
counter after a count.

The area of the cross section of the inside of the quartz tube,
checked beforehand, was 8.1×10^{-3} cm². Thus the volume of helium in the tube was

$$\text{Volume} = \text{length} \times \text{area of cross section}$$
$$= 5.0 \text{ cm} \times 8.1 \times 10^{-3} \text{ cm}^2$$
$$= 4.0 \times 10^{-2} \text{ cm}^3.$$

The density of helium at atmospheric pressure and room temperature is 1.7×10^{-4} g/cm³. The mass of the sample of helium is

$$\text{Mass} = \text{volume} \times \text{density}$$
$$= 4.0 \times 10^{-2} \text{ cm}^3 \times 1.7 \times 10^{-4} \text{ g/cm}^3$$
$$= 6.8 \times 10^{-6} \text{ g}.$$

Dilution

The small sample of polonium was first dissolved in 1.0×10^3 cm³ of nitric acid. Therefore, one cubic centimeter of this solution contains $\frac{1}{1,000}$ of the original amount of polonium.

A volume of 1.0 cm³ of this solution was then mixed with 99 cm³ of water. Hence 1.0 cm³ of this dilute solution contained only 1 part in 10^5 (or 1.0×10^{-5}) of the original sample of polonium. Even this was too much to be counted!

Therefore, only 1.0×10^{-3} cm³ (one one-thousandth of a cubic centimeter) of the very dilute polonium solution was placed on the plate to be counted. This meant that only $1.0 \times 10^{-5} \times 1.0 \times 10^{-3} = 1.0 \times 10^{-8}$, or 1 part in 100 million, of the original polonium was counted. Two trials were run with samples of this size.

Counting

Trial 1: 2.4×10^5 counts/minute

Trial 2: 2.0×10^5 counts/minute

This step introduces the largest experimental error in the experiment so far. The average of the two readings, 2.2×10^5 counts/minute, was used.

The counter used in the experiment described above does not count those helium particles which fly off into the plate; it counts only those which fly off upward (Figure 11.9). Thus the true disintegration rate was twice the recorded number, or 4.4×10^5 counts/minute.

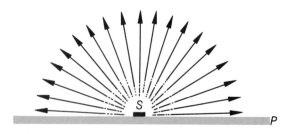

Figure 11.9
Helium particles flying off from a thin polonium source *S* on a metal plate *P*. Those emitted in the directions shown by the arrows can be counted. Half of the helium particles are emitted downward into the plate and are not counted.

This large number of counts comes from only 1.0×10^{-8} of the original sample. The number of disintegrations per minute of the whole sample is $1.0 \times 10^8 \times 4.4 \times 10^5 = 4.4 \times 10^{13}$ counts/minute.

Now let us recall that the quartz tube containing the polonium was sealed on March 3 and opened on March 24. This is a period of 21 days or $21 \times 24 \times 60 = 3.0 \times 10^4$ minutes.

If the sample of polonium had decayed at the same rate of 4.4×10^{13} counts/minute over the entire duration of the experiment, then the total number of counts would have been the product

$$4.4 \times 10^{13} \text{ counts/minute} \times 3.0 \times 10^4 \text{ minute} = 1.3 \times 10^{18} \text{ counts.}$$

We know that this cannot be exactly the case because there are more polonium atoms at the beginning of the experiment than at the end. The number of disintegrations per minute must also be less at the end. But as we shall see in the next section, the error introduced by ignoring this change in the rate of decay is smaller than the uncertainty in the measurement of the 10^{-3}-cm^3 sample of the dilute solution. Therefore, we shall use the value 1.3×10^{18} for the total number of counts during the experiment.

We said earlier that we shall assume that each count signals the formation of one helium atom. Thus the number of helium atoms produced by the polonium sample during the three weeks is:

$$\text{Number of atoms} = 1.3 \times 10^{18}$$

and the mass of one helium atom is

$$\text{Mass of atom} = \frac{\text{mass of sample}}{\text{number of atoms in sample}}$$

$$= \frac{6.8 \times 10^{-6} \text{ g}}{1.3 \times 10^{18}} = 5.2 \times 10^{-24} \text{ g.}$$

---

9 If the mass of an atom of an element is 5.0×10^{-23} g, how many atoms are there in 1 g of that element?

10† A cylindrical tube with a cross-sectional area of 2 cm^2 and a height of 50 cm is filled with hydrogen. What is the volume of the hydrogen in the tube?

11 Write a brief summary of the steps followed in finding the mass of helium atoms by radioactive decay.

12† In the experiment on the mass of helium, how many lead atoms were formed? What assumptions are made to get this number?

11.5   THE MASS OF POLONIUM ATOMS

We can apply the relation

$$\text{Mass of atom} = \frac{\text{mass of sample}}{\text{number of atoms in sample}}$$

to polonium as well as to helium. We assumed that one atom of polonium disintegrates into one atom of lead and one atom of helium. Therefore, the number of atoms of polonium that disintegrated during the three weeks of the experiment equals the number of helium atoms formed. This number we calculated in the preceding section. To calculate the mass of one polonium atom, we must know the mass of the polonium that disintegrated.

The decay of polonium and other radioactive elements has been studied extensively. In all cases it has been found that the rate of decay—that is, the number of disintegrations per minute—is proportional to the number of atoms of the radioactive element in the sample. If we start, for example, with a sample of pure polonium, the rate of decay will get smaller and smaller as disintegration proceeds and fewer polonium atoms remain in the sample.

The rate of decay of polonium as a function of time is shown in Figure 11.10. A value of one has been chosen as the initial rate. This enables us to use the graph for any sample of polonium. For example, you can read from the graph that the rate of decay after 21 days is 0.90 of the initial rate.*

---

*As you can see, in the time the tube was closed, the rate of decay of the polonium had decreased by only about 10 percent. Since we had a difference of almost 20 percent in our measurements of the counting rate of our two 10^{-8} fractions, we were justified within the accuracy of our experiment in assuming that the disintegration rate was constant and equal to 4.4×10^{13} helium atoms/minute in the quartz tube.

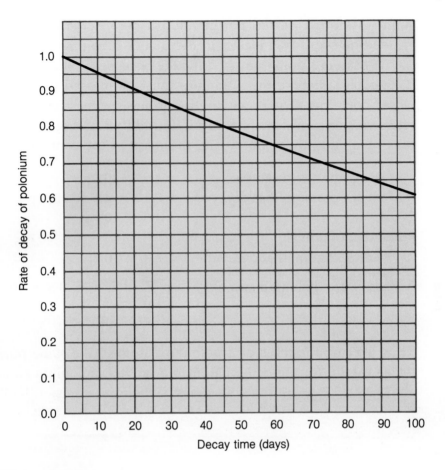

Figure 11.10
The rate of decay of a sample containing polonium as a function of
time. The rate (number of polonium atoms disintegrating per unit
time) is expressed in terms of the fraction of the rate measured at zero
days.

The rate of decay in Figure 11.10 is proportional to the
fraction of the polonium remaining. For example, if only half the
polonium remains, the rate of decay will be half of what it was
originally. Since after 21 days the rate of decay was 0.90 of the
original rate, 0.90 of the original mass of polonium still remained in
the quartz tube. In other words, 0.10 of the initial sample had
decayed.

All this we learn from Figure 11.10. But to find out how much
polonium decayed, we have to know the initial mass of the polo-

nium. Although we did not mention it before, the polonium was massed before it was placed in the quartz tube (Figure 11.11).

Massing polonium is difficult. Because of the intense and dangerous radiation, the polonium must be massed inside a small closed container. The procedure resembles the massing of a liquid. Here we quote only the final result, found by massing the container plus polonium, then subtracting the mass of the container.

Mass of polonium sample $= 4.5 \times 10^{-3}$ g

Mass of polonium that decayed $= 0.10 \times 4.5 \times 10^{-3}$ g
$= 4.5 \times 10^{-4}$ g

Number of atoms
of polonium that decayed $= 1.3 \times 10^{18}$

Mass of one polonium atom $= \dfrac{4.5 \times 10^{-4}}{1.3 \times 10^{18}} = 3.5 \times 10^{-22}$ g
$= 350 \times 10^{-24}$ g

Thus, writing the mass of a polonium atom to the same power of ten as we did for the helium atom, we see that polonium atoms are about $350/5.2 = 67$ times as heavy as helium atoms.

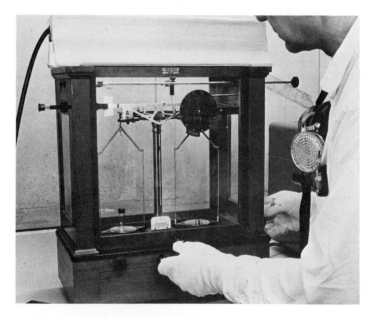

Figure 11.11
A few milligrams of polonium being weighed on a sensitive balance. The polonium is in a small glass tube in the sealed bottle on the left-hand pan. The bottle is sealed to prevent dangerous contamination of the balance and the laboratory by the polonium.

The two experiments involve the determination of the mass and number of atoms in a small sample. They are by no means the first or the most accurate of such determinations, but they are perhaps the most direct. A repetition of this experiment, which you may see in an *IPS* film, gave a similar result: 7.5×10^{-24} g for helium and 410×10^{-24} g for polonium. For higher precision, different methods are used and give a mass of 6.64×10^{-24} g for helium and 349×10^{-24} g for polonium.

Before studying this experiment, you had no way of guessing even vaguely what the mass of a single atom might be. The mass might have been a billion times larger than 10^{-24} g—that is, about 10^{-15} g—or perhaps 10^{-33} g, a billion times smaller. Thus, being able to conclude that the mass of a helium atom is close to 6×10^{-24} g is an impressive achievement.

13 **Write a brief summary of the steps followed in finding the mass of polonium atoms by radioactive decay.**

14 **In Experiment 11.3, you determined the mass of an oleic acid molecule. How many atoms would this molecule contain if the mass of each atom equaled (a) the mass of a helium atom or (b) the mass of a polonium atom?**

11.6   THE NUMBER OF PARTICLES IN A MOLE: AVOGADRO'S NUMBER

In section 8.10 we called the number of carbon atoms in 12.0 g of carbon a mole. The ratio of the mass of a helium atom to that of a carbon atom is 4.00/12.0 (Table 8.4). Therefore, 4.00 g of helium also contains a mole of helium atoms. Now that we have determined the mass of a single helium atom, we can calculate the number of helium atoms in a mole of helium using the following relationship:

$$\text{Number of atoms in a mole} = \frac{\text{mass of a mole of helium atoms}}{\text{mass of one helium atom}}$$

$$= \frac{4.00 \text{ g}}{6.64 \times 10^{-24} \text{ g}} = 6.02 \times 10^{23}$$

This number is called "Avogadro's number." It is a very large number indeed. Just think how many atoms make up even the smallest piece of paper that you can mass on your *IPS* balance!

---

15 a) What is the mass of a mole of iron atoms? (See Table 8.4.)
    b) How many atoms are there in a mole of iron atoms?

16 a) What is the mass of a mole of nitrogen atoms?
    b) Nitrogen molecules contain two nitrogen atoms (N_2). What is the mass of a mole of nitrogen molecules?
    c) How many nitrogen atoms are there in a mole of nitrogen molecules?

17† How many atoms of aluminum are there in 1.0×10^{-3} g of aluminum?

11.7   THE SIZE OF ATOMS

Earlier in this chapter you found the size of a molecule of oleic acid. But a molecule of oleic acid is made up of many atoms. What is the size of a single atom? How can it be found?

To find the mass of a single atom we used the relation

$$\text{Mass of one atom} = \frac{\text{mass of sample}}{\text{number of atoms in sample}}.$$

Can we use the relation

$$\text{Volume of one atom} = \frac{\text{volume of sample}}{\text{number of atoms in sample}}$$

to find the volume of one atom? If we can find the volume of an atom and assume a specific shape for it, we can find its size.

To answer the question above, consider the following analogy. Calculating the volume of one student by dividing the volume of the classroom by the number of students will surely be misleading. There is plenty of empty space between any two students. However, finding the volume of one person by dividing the volume of an elevator by the number of people packed tightly in it, may give more reliable results.

In section 8.9 we related the incompressibility of solids to the idea that in solids atoms "touch" each other. Therefore, for solids the above relation makes sense.

As a sample we can choose a mole of atoms. Then

$$\text{Volume of one atom} = \frac{\text{volume of one mole of atoms}}{\text{Avogadro's number}}.$$

The volume of one mole of atoms of any element can be calculated from the atomic masses (Table 8.4) and the densities (Table 3.1) of the elements:

$$\text{Volume of one mole} = \frac{\text{mass of one mole of atoms}}{\text{density of the element}}$$

For example, from Table 8.4 the mass of one mole of copper atoms is 63.5 g. The density of copper, from Table 3.1, is 8.9 g/cm³. Therefore:

$$\text{Volume of one mole of copper atoms} = \frac{63.5 \text{ g}}{8.9 \text{ g/cm}^3} = 7.1 \text{ cm}^3.$$

Finally,

$$\text{Volume of one atom of copper} = \frac{7.1 \text{ cm}^3}{6.02 \times 10^{23}} = 1.2 \times 10^{-23} \text{ cm}^3.$$

If we were to think of copper atoms as tiny cubes, then the length of the edge of the cube would be

$$\sqrt[3]{1.2 \times 10^{-23} \text{ cm}^3} = 2.3 \times 10^{-8} \text{ cm}.$$

If we think of copper atoms as tiny spheres enclosed in these cubes, then the diameter of the sphere will be 2.3×10^{-8} cm (Figure 11.12). The diameters of other atoms are shown in Table 11.1.

None of the experiments that you have done in this course suggest any particular shape for atoms. The values of the diameters in Table 11.1 should be considered only as a general indication of size. As such, the table is truly remarkable. The masses of atoms (second column) vary over a factor of about 200, but their diameters (fifth column) hardly vary at all. Unlike people, heavier atoms are not necessarily bigger! This observation raises new questions about the structure of the atoms themselves.

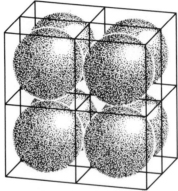

Figure 11.12
Spheres touching all faces of the cubes containing them. The diameter of the spheres equals the length of the edge of the cubes.

---

18   The relative mass of a silver atom is 108 u. The density of silver is 10.5 g/cm³. What is the volume of one mole of silver atoms?

19   a)   Use Table 8.4 and the class results of Experiment 3.7: The Density of Solids to calculate the volume of one iron atom.
b)   By comparing your result for (a) with the atomic volumes in Table 11.1, estimate the size of an iron atom.

20   The densities of elements do not change much when the elements melt. On the basis of this information, can you use the methods developed in this section to calculate the volume of an atom in a liquid? Explain your answer.

Table 11.1

Element	Mass of one mole of atoms (g)	Density (g/cm³)	Volume of one atom (cm³)	Diameter of one atom (cm)
Aluminum	27.0	2.70	1.7×10^{-23}	2.6×10^{-8}
Bromine (Liquid)	79.9	3.12	4.3×10^{-23}	3.5×10^{-8}
Copper	63.5	8.90	1.2×10^{-23}	2.3×10^{-8}
Helium (Liquid)	4.0	0.15	4.4×10^{-23}	3.5×10^{-8}
Hydrogen (Liquid)	1.01	0.07	2.4×10^{-23}	2.9×10^{-8}
Gold	197.0	19.3	1.7×10^{-23}	2.6×10^{-8}
Lithium	6.94	0.53	2.2×10^{-23}	2.8×10^{-8}
Platinum	195.0	21.4	1.5×10^{-23}	2.5×10^{-8}
Polonium	210.0	9.4	3.7×10^{-23}	3.3×10^{-8}

For Home, Desk, and Lab

21 A rectangular object 3.0 cm × 4.0 cm × 5.0 cm is made of many tiny cubes, each 1.0×10^{-2} cm on an edge. How many cubes does the object contain?

22 The diameter of a tennis ball is about 0.07 m, and the dimensions of a tennis court are 15 m × 30 m. How many tennis balls will be required to cover the court?

23 If the molecules of the oleic acid layer you made could be placed end to end in a line, about how long would it be?

24 If a 10^{-3}-g sample of radium gives a count of 4×10^7 counts/minute, how much radium would give 100 counts/minute?

25 Suppose you buy a 2-kg bag of dried beans and you find it has been contaminated with small stones. How would you go about finding the approximate number of the stones in the bag without separating all the stones in the bag from the beans? What assumptions have you made?

26 A cubic millimeter (10^{-3} cm^3) of blood is found to contain about 5×10^6 red blood cells. An adult human body contains about 5×10^3 cm^3 of blood. About how many red blood cells are there in an adult human body?

27 Some polonium is dissolved in 1,000 cm^3 of nitric acid, and a 0.01-cm^3 sample of the solution is counted. Then the number of disintegrations per minute is found to be 3×10^3. How many disintegrations per minute occurred in the original solution?

28 If 10^{18} atoms of polonium disintegrate to produce lead and 10^{-5} g of helium, what is the mass of a helium atom?

29 Use Figure 11.10 to determine the fraction of a polonium sample that remains after 45 days. What fraction of the polonium decayed during this time?

30 a) What fraction of a sample of pure polonium will decay in 100 days? (See Figure 11.10.)
b) If a counter initially records 5×10^4 counts/minute for the sample, what would you expect it to record after 100 days?

31 What would you get for the volume of one atom of helium if you calculated it from the equation below?

$$\text{Volume of one atom} = \frac{\text{volume of gas sample}}{\text{number of atoms in gas sample}}$$

32 A penny is about 1 mm thick. About how many layers of copper atoms does it contain?

33 In Experiment 6.4, a student found that 2.25 g of zinc combined with chlorine to form 4.72 g of zinc chloride.

a) How many moles of zinc atoms reacted?

b) How many moles of chlorine atoms combined with this mass of zinc?

c) How many atoms of each element combined in this reaction?

Themes for Short Essays

1   A few grains of sand can be placed on an overhead projector and projected on the wall. The images are large enough to be measured with a ruler. To be able to calculate the size of the grains of sand, you also need to project an object of known size. Do this investigation and find the size of one sand grain. Then, using the results of your own experimentation on the volume of sand (Experiment 2.3), write a research report, "The Number of Sand Grains in a Cup of Sand."

2   Write an experimental section for an *IBS* (*Introductory Biological Science*) textbook to count the hairs on your head.

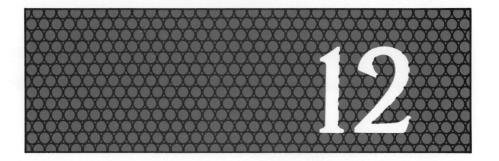

Molecular Motion

12.1 MOLECULAR MOTION AND DIFFUSION

When we put a piece of wood on a table, it stays there. But as soon as we take the cap off a bottle of ammonia solution, some of the gas comes out of the solution, escapes into the air, and spreads in all directions. On a cold winter day, some of the hot water in a bathtub evaporates and spreads throughout the room, condensing on the cold windowpanes and walls. Water vapor, a gas, moves from the tub in all directions. If a gas spreads all by itself, we have to conclude that its molecules are in motion.

To demonstrate that the molecules of a gas move around freely, we find it convenient to use a gas that is visible and that can be liquefied easily. The element bromine has both these properties: It has a deep red-brown color and will solidify when cooled by a mixture of dry ice and alcohol.

The photograph on the far left in Figure 12.1 shows a sealed glass tube containing a small quantity of bromine and, of course, air. The tube was cooled by a mixture of dry ice and alcohol. All the bromine is seen as a solid at the bottom of the tube.

The other photographs, moving from left to right, show the tube at different times while it was warming. You can clearly see that, as the bromine evaporates, it moves slowly upward until it is evenly distributed throughout the tube. This set of pictures suggests that the bromine molecules must move around very slowly.

To be sure that the experiment shown in Figure 12.1 really

Figure 12.1
A series of photographs, taken at different times, of a sealed glass tube containing bromine. In the photograph at the far left, taken immediately after the tube was removed from a mixture of dry ice and alcohol, the bromine is all at the bottom of the tube as a solid. As the tube warms up, the bromine turns to liquid and evaporates. Brown bromine gas slowly spreads upward, gradually darkening the tube until the gas is evenly distributed.

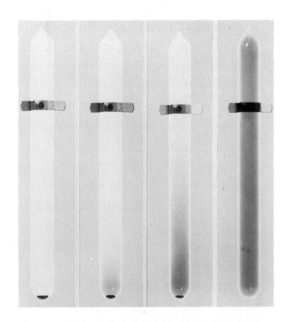

tells us something about the speed of the bromine molecules, we have to repeat the experiment with bromine but no air (or at least almost no air) in the tube.

Figure 12.2 shows a set of pictures of a tube containing a little bromine and very little air. Most of the air was pumped out, and the tube was sealed while the bromine was frozen. Then the tube was allowed to warm up in the same way as the tube in Figure 12.1.

Figure 12.2
The tube shown in this series of photographs is the same as that shown in Figure 12.1, except that there is practically no air in it. It was photographed at the same intervals as the tube in Figure 12.1. Note that as the bromine evaporates, it fills the tube evenly, coloring the whole tube a darker and darker shade. Unlike the process shown in Figure 12.1, this time the gas moves quickly up the tube.

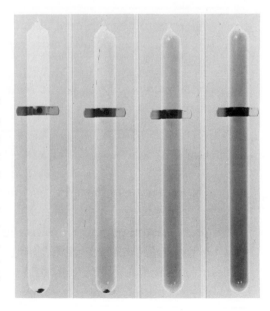

Note that almost as soon as the faintest color is observed, the color is the same throughout the tube. The color gets darker as the tube warms up and more bromine evaporates, but if you covered up the two ends of the tube with your hands, you could hardly tell which end contained the solid bromine. Contrast this with Figure 12.1, where there is no doubt which way the bromine is moving. Evidently, when there is no air in the tube, the bromine molecules move so fast that they bounce back and forth and distribute themselves evenly inside the tube so quickly we cannot perceive it.

We can now understand why the bromine molecules seemed to move so slowly in the tube containing air (Figure 12.1). Think of a group of runners trying to spread out across a football field on which several hundred people are milling around. Even if moving at top speed, a runner, after only a few steps, will bump into someone. The runner may be pushed aside a little, or may even be thrown backward. The next collision will have similar results. What would otherwise be a straight dash across the field becomes a zigzag path. It is no wonder that under such circumstances it will be a long time before even a few of the runners reach the other side of the field. In this picture, the group of runners plays the role of the evaporating bromine; the milling crowd, that of the air in the tube.

To sum up, molecules of a gas apparently bounce around at high speeds. Because of the many collisions, one gas spreads through another rather slowly. This process of one gas spreading through another is called "diffusion."

1 What would be different about the photographs in Figure 12.1 if (*a*) the bromine evaporated more rapidly or (*b*) there were more air in the tube?

2 What evidence leads you to believe that atoms are in motion and not at rest?

12.2   DENSITY AND PRESSURE OF A GAS

By using fasteners and rings to illustrate the atomic model, we were able to make a prediction about how elements combine to form compounds. We confirmed this prediction with our test of two chlorides of copper. When we used fasteners and rings, they were at rest. They were not in constant zigzag motion as we know the molecules of a gas are. If we wish to predict the properties of gases made up of rapidly moving molecules, we must extend the atomic model to include the motion of molecules. To illustrate the motion of the molecules in a gas and to help us predict some effects of this motion, we shall use small steel spheres. Of course, steel spheres do not stay forever in motion on their own. If we want to study steel balls that are bouncing over a period of time, we have to keep them in motion. We can do this with the apparatus shown in Figures 12.3 and 12.4.

The spheres inside the cylinder (Figure 12.3) are resting on a movable platform connected to an electric motor. A plastic disk is resting on top of the spheres. When the motor is turned on, the platform moves rapidly up and down over a short distance, keeping the spheres in motion.

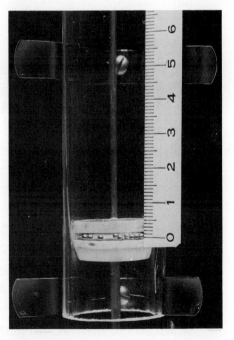

Figure 12.3
A plastic cylinder, with a movable platform near the bottom, contains some small steel spheres and a movable disk lying on top of the spheres. The movable platform is vibrated up and down by a shaft connected to a small electric motor.

Figure 12.4
A close-up view of the movable platform, spheres, and disk shown in Figure 12.3.

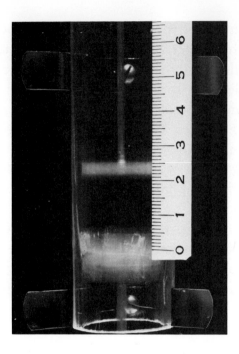

Figure 12.5
The cylinder shown in Figure 12.4, with the bottom platform being vibrated rapidly up and down over a short distance by an electric motor. The photograph is a time exposure of 4 seconds.

Figure 12.5 shows what happened to the plastic disk when the motor was turned on. The shutter of the camera was open for 4 seconds. During this time, the little spheres bounced around so many times that in the figure they have been smeared out and are practically invisible. Yet their presence is very much in evidence. Note that the disk is now held at a position well up the cylinder. This is caused by the moving spheres bouncing off the bottom of the disk.

In Figure 12.5, there are 10 spheres in the tube. How does the volume of the "sphere gas" change if we double the number of spheres in the tube? Figure 12.6 gives us the answer: The volume has increased; in fact, it has almost doubled. To get the spheres back to the volume they occupied before we doubled their number, we have to add to the mass of the disk. With twice the mass pushing down on the spheres, we find that a sample of sphere gas containing 20 spheres occupies the same volume as a sample with 10 spheres held down by the original mass (Figure 12.7). In other words, twice as many spheres bouncing around in the same volume push up on the disk twice as hard. This suggests that the contribution of each sphere to holding up the disk is independent of that of all the other spheres. If we double the number of spheres, while keeping the volume constant, they will be able to support a disk of twice the mass.

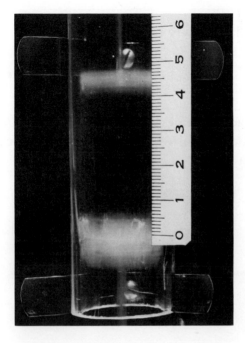

Figure 12.6
With twice as many steel spheres in the cylinder as in Figure 12.5, the volume of the "sphere gas" is close to twice as great as the volume shown in Figure 12.5.

Doubling the number of spheres doubles the pressure the spheres exert on the bottom of the disk. The mass of the spheres is not important: Doubling the number of light spheres or doubling the number of heavy spheres doubles the pressure.

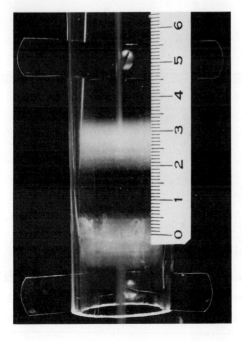

Figure 12.7
Adding a second disk, whose mass equals that of the original disk, reduces the volume occupied by 20 spheres to that occupied by the 10 in Figure 12.5.

3† If a gas is compressed until its pressure is doubled, what will happen to the density of the gas?

4 In the sphere-gas machine, what would you expect to happen if the top disk had less mass?

5 Two bricks are placed on each of three wood dowels resting on clay as shown in Figure A. Which dowel will sink fastest into the clay? On which is the pressure greatest?

Figure A
For problem 5

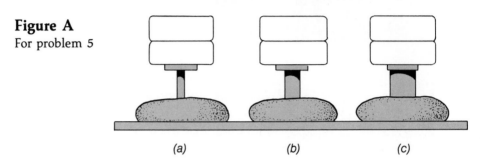

(a)   (b)   (c)

6 Two bricks are placed on each of the pistons shown in Figure B. In which cylinder will the pressure of the gas be greatest?

Figure B
For problem 6

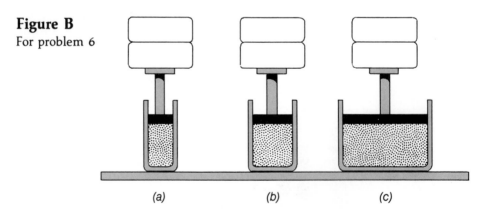

(a)   (b)   (c)

12.3 A PREDICTION ABOUT THE RELATION BETWEEN VOLUME AND PRESSURE OF GASES

Imagine a quantity of gas contained in a cylinder equipped with a piston like that shown in Figure 12.8. The piston corresponds to the disk in the sphere-gas machine. If we double the number of mole-

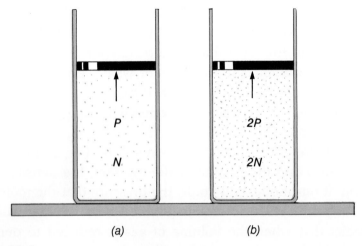

Figure 12.8
(*a*) There are N molecules in the cylinder. (*b*) If we double the number of molecules in the cylinder and the piston is kept in the same position as in (*a*), the pressure P exerted by the gas will double.

cules of gas while keeping the volume constant, we double the density of the gas. The pressure exerted by the gas on the bottom of the piston will also double.

Forcing more gas into a given volume is not the only way to increase its density. We can also increase the density of a gas by keeping its mass constant and decreasing its volume. Consider a cylinder containing a gas (Figure 12.9). In Figure 12.9(*a*) there are $2N$

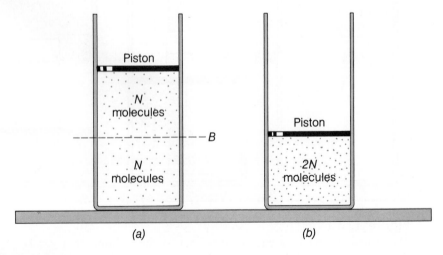

Figure 12.9
Halving the volume of a gas by moving the piston down to B will double the density and, we predict, double the pressure.

molecules: N molecules in the upper half and N molecules in the lower half. If we push the piston down to B, we shall then have $2N$ molecules in the lower half (Figure 12.9[b]). The density of the gas will have doubled. On the basis of what we have seen in the preceding section, we can expect that the gas will exert a pressure that is twice as great as the pressure exerted when the piston was at the top of the cylinder.

If we push the piston down still farther, so that it is halfway between B and the bottom of the cylinder, the density will double again. If our model still holds, the pressure that the molecules exert on the piston will also double (Figure 12.10). In other words, we can predict that when the volume of gas is reduced to one-fourth its original volume, the pressure will increase to four times the original pressure.

We can generalize our predictions by saying that if we *decrease* the volume of a gas by a certain factor, the pressure of the gas will *increase* by the same factor. This relationship is illustrated in Figure 12.11.

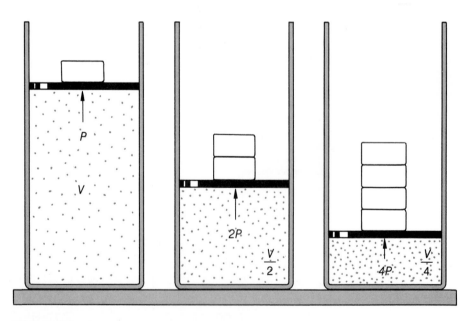

Figure 12.10
The atomic model of a gas predicts that as the volume of a gas is decreased, its pressure rises in the manner shown by the three diagrams.

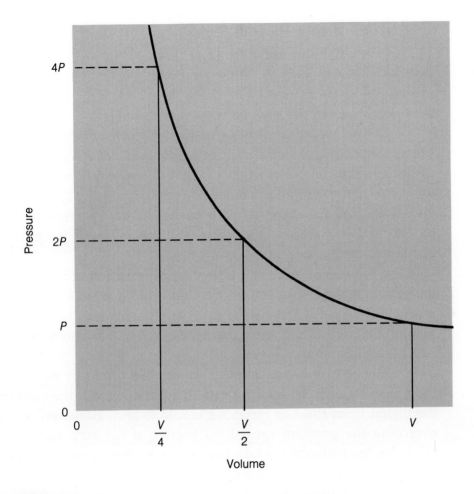

Figure 12.11
A graph of the pressure of a gas as a function of its volume, as predicted from the atomic model.

Note that in developing our argument, we have made two basic assumptions: (a) The molecules of a gas are constantly in motion, and (b) the bouncing of one molecule off the wall of a container is not affected by the presence of other gas molecules. We made no assumptions as to how many atoms, or atoms of what elements, are in a molecule of the gas. Thus, if the predicted relation between the pressure and volume of a gas is at all correct, it should hold true for all gases as long as the two basic assumptions mentioned here are correct.

262

12.4 THE COMPRESSIBILITY OF GASES

The apparatus shown in Figure 12.12 was used to check the prediction we have just made about the relation between the pressure and the volume of air. By adding bricks to the platform on the top of the syringe, the air in the syringe was compressed.

Before we added bricks to the platform, we adjusted the initial volume of gas in the syringe to about 30 cm³. We did this by pushing the piston down while a length of string was held between the inside of the syringe and the piston seal (Figure 12.13). The string allows air to escape as the piston is pushed down. When we reached the 30 cm³, we pulled out the string. With this volume, the piston is stable enough to hold up to four bricks.

Our procedure is complicated by the effect of friction. When the piston is pushed down, friction prevents it from *sinking* as far down as it would if there were no friction. This results in a larger volume than we would expect from our prediction about the relation of volume and pressure.

The reverse happens when we remove bricks. If we remove them, one by one, the sticking caused by friction will then prevent the piston from *rising* as far as we would expect. However, we can overcome the problem caused by friction if for each number of bricks on the platform we take two readings of each volume, one as we put them on and one as we take them off. Taking the average of each pair of readings very nearly cancels the error introduced by friction.

After adjusting the initial volume and before adding the first brick, we pulled the platform up a little and let it fall until it settled. We then recorded the volume for "zero bricks."

Next, we added one brick and, without giving it any downward push, let it come to rest and recorded the volume. We continued to add bricks and record volume in the same way until we reached a total of four bricks. At this point we had half our volume measurements—those for the piston as it moved down under the pressure of more and more bricks. To obtain volume measurements for the piston on the way up, we first pushed down slightly on the four bricks. After removing our hand, the piston rose, but nevertheless came to rest slightly below its resting point before we gave our push. This resting point gave us our second reading for the largest number of bricks.

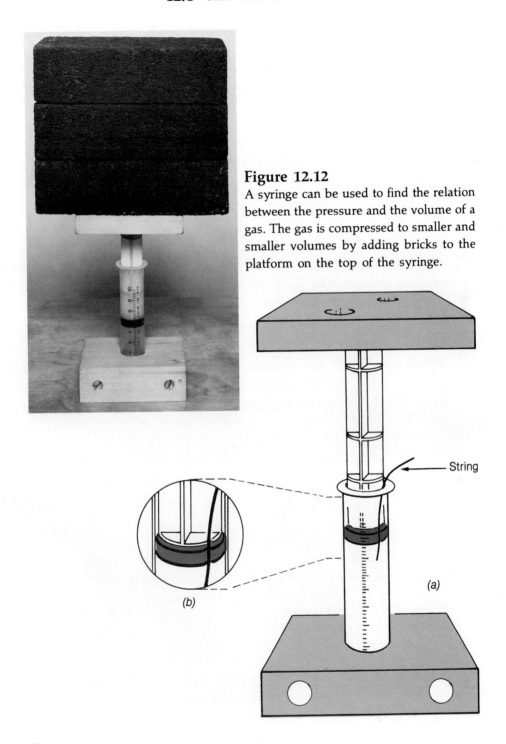

Figure 12.12
A syringe can be used to find the relation between the pressure and the volume of a gas. The gas is compressed to smaller and smaller volumes by adding bricks to the platform on the top of the syringe.

String

(a)

(b)

Figure 12.13
The inset in (b) shows how a piece of string is used to hold open the seal of the syringe in (a) when adjusting the initial volume of air in the syringe.

Table 12.1

| Down | | Up | | |
number of bricks	volume (cm³)	number of bricks	volume (cm³)	Average volume (cm³)
0	30.0	0	28.4	29.2
1	22.6	1	20.0	21.3
2	17.8	2	15.7	16.8
3	14.1	3	12.8	13.5
4	11.7	4	10.9	11.3

We then removed the bricks one-by-one and recorded each volume in turn. The data we obtained are shown in Table 12.1.

Figure 12.14 shows the graph of these data. It looks much like Figure 12.11. Both show that the pressure increases when the volume decreases. But a careful examination reveals that there is a significant difference: When the volume is halved from 25 to 12.5 cm³, the pressure goes from about 0.5 bricks to 3.4 bricks, not up to 1.0 brick, as we should expect on the basis of Figure 12.11. Similarly, when we

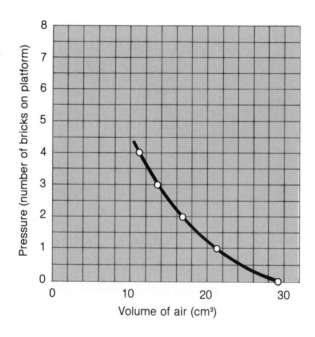

Figure 12.14
The pressure of a gas (air) as a function of volume. The data are plotted from Table 12.1. Note that when the volume is halved, the pressure does not double.

increased the pressure from 1 to 2 bricks, the volume was reduced from 21.3 to 16.8 cm^3, and not to about 10.7 cm^3, as we might expect. Is the theory wrong?

Let us look again at the details of the experiment described in this section. We started with no bricks on the wooden platform and then added them one at a time until we reached four. But actually the bricks were not all that pressed on the gas in the cylinder. The piston, the wooden platform on which the bricks were resting, and the air above the cylinder were all pressing on the gas. Thus, when we replace one brick with two bricks, we do not double the pressure.

To get the total pressure on the gas, we must add to the pressure exerted by the bricks the pressure caused by the platform, the piston, and the air. How much pressure, in terms of bricks, must we add? Suppose that we add one brick. This would raise every point on the curve one unit. Had we done this, we would have found it to be not enough.

By trial and error we found that raising each point on the curve of Figure 12.14 by the equivalent of 2.4 bricks makes a curve that agrees closely with Figure 12.11. Our result is shown in Figure 12.15. In Figure 12.15, doubling the pressure halves the volume. For

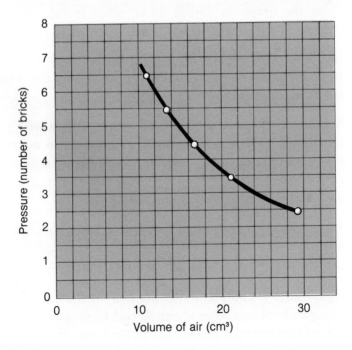

Figure 12.15
The same graph as shown in Figure 12.14, but with the curve moved vertically upward by 2.4 bricks on the pressure scale.

example, when we go from 3 to 6 bricks, the volume decreases from 24.0 cm^3 to 12.1 cm^3, which is very close to one-half of the initial volume. Our prediction, made from the atomic model of a gas, is indeed borne out by our measurements of the pressure and the corresponding volume of air as it is compressed in a cylinder by different numbers of bricks.

The experiment has been repeated with other gases, such as carbon dioxide and propane. If the initial volume is the same as in Figure 12.14, and the same syringe and bricks are used, the graphs are the same for air, carbon dioxide, propane, and other gases. In other words, under the conditions of our experiment, different gases have the same compressibility. Our model predicted this behavior of gases.

The relationship we have found between the pressure and the volume of a gas was discovered by Robert Boyle in 1662 and bears the name "Boyle's law." We predicted Boyle's law from the atomic model. Boyle discovered the law by doing experiments similar to the one we have described in this section. This was before there was an atomic model for gases from which Boyle's law could have been predicted.

7† From the graph in Figure 12.11, what is the pressure when the volume is reduced (a) from V to $\frac{1}{3}V$, (b) from V to $\frac{3}{4}V$?

8 In Figure 12.15, when the total pressure is doubled by increasing from 2.5 bricks to 5 bricks, what is the ratio of the initial volume to the final volume?

9 A cylinder contains 1,000 cm^3 of hydrogen at a total pressure of 1.0 atmosphere. What will be the total pressure in atmospheres if the temperature does not change and the volume is reduced to:
a) 100 cm^3?
b) 10 cm^3?

10† A cylinder contains 100 cm^3 of air at a total pressure P (pressure due to piston plus atmospheric pressure). What will the total pressure become if the volume is reduced to (a) 50 cm^3, (b) 10 cm^3?

11 Figure 12.15 is a graph of pressure as a function of volume of air over a range of volume from about 30 cm^3 to about 10 cm^3. What would you predict the total pressure to be (in terms of bricks) if the volume of gas were (a) 10 cm^3, (b) 70 cm^3?

12.5 BEHAVIOR OF GASES AT HIGH PRESSURES

We have seen that gases have the same compressibility at pressures near atmospheric pressure. What happens if we compress gases to very high pressures?

Figure 12.16 is a graph of volume as a function of pressure for

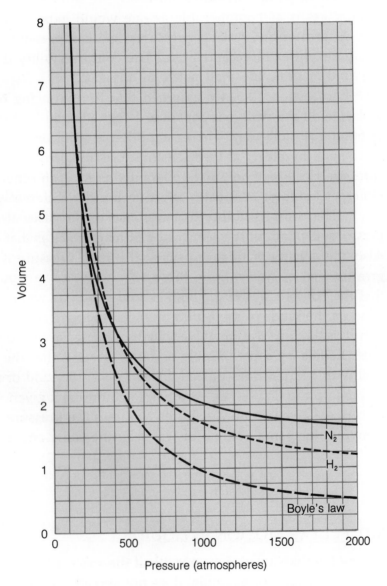

Figure 12.16
The different compressibilities of different gases at high pressure are shown by this graph of the volume as a function of pressure for nitrogen and hydrogen at 0°C. The lowest dashed line is the curve a gas would have if it satisfied Boyle's law at high pressure.

nitrogen and hydrogen at very high pressures and at 0°C. The lowest curve is the graph that could be predicted for both gases by Boyle's law. You can see that both gases follow Boyle's law at pressures less than approximately 150 atmospheres. It is impossible to distinguish between the two gases by their compressibility at relatively low pressures.

At very high pressures, however, the story is quite different. Neither gas is as compressible as one would expect from Boyle's law. At greater and greater pressures, the compressibilities of the two gases differ more and more. The compressibility depends on the kind of molecule that makes up the gas.

In section 12.3, we assumed that the bouncing of one gas molecule off the wall of a container is not affected by the presence of other gas molecules. This assumption is valid only at low pressures and, therefore, at low densities. Gas molecules at high pressures are close together, and apparently affect each other's motion. Different kinds of molecules affect each other differently.

The compressibility that we observe for gases at such high pressures is of about the same order of magnitude as that of liquids. Also, the density of nitrogen gas at this high pressure is nearly as great as that of water. From these observations, we would predict that the compressibility of liquids (and solids as well) should depend on the kinds of molecules of which they are composed. Such, in fact, is the case. Although very high pressures are needed to compress liquids by a measurable amount, we find that the compressibility of a liquid does indeed depend upon the kind of molecules making up the liquid. For example, to compress a given volume of glycerine a given amount requires 2.5 times the pressure needed to compress the same volume of water by the same amount.

12.6   MOLECULAR MOTION IN LIQUIDS

A liquid, unlike a gas, does not fill all the space available to it. The water in a glass, for example, does not spread throughout a room. Does this mean that the molecules in a liquid do not move? There is a simple though slow way to show that molecules in a liquid do move. Figure 12.17 shows a series of photographs of a graduated cylinder containing a water solution of copper sulfate and pure water. In the first photograph, the more dense, dark copper sulfate solution is in the bottom half, with pure water floating on top of it. After several days, you can see that the division between the two liquids is no longer sharp. Some of the blue copper sulfate has diffused up into the water, making it slightly colored. Notice that after about 19 weeks the copper sulfate is spread almost evenly throughout the cylinder. This is like the behavior of bromine gas diffusing into air (section 12.1), except that the copper sulfate dif-

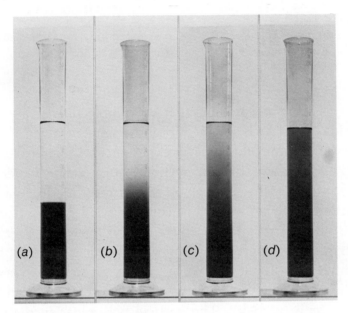

Figure 12.17
The diffusion of copper sulfate solution into water. (*a*) At the start of the experiment the copper sulfate solution and the water form two distinct layers. (*b*) Five days later. (*c*) Thirty-seven days later. (*d*) One hundred thirty-four days later.

fuses through water much more slowly. This is what we should expect, since in a liquid the molecules are much closer together than they are in a gas. Even if they move at about the same speeds as molecules in a gas, molecules in a liquid can move only a very short distance before hitting and bouncing off other molecules.

As you already know, molecules are too small to be seen even through a powerful microscope. However, there are particles that are large enough to be seen in a microscope yet small enough to be pushed around by the jostling molecules of water. To understand their motion we start with a model. For simplicity, we will consider only motion in a plane. Furthermore, for reasons that will become clear in the next section, we shall assume that the particles have the shape of a hexagon (Figure 12.18).

Figure 12.18
The assumed shape of a "particle" suspended in water. A hexagon is shown for convenience only; the actual shape is not important.

Our model assumes that water molecules hit the particle from all sides. Will each side be hit by the same number of molecules in every short time interval? Our experience with radioactive decay can help us make a prediction (section 7.10). Averaged over many short time intervals, the number of counts per time interval was nearly constant. But the number of counts varied greatly from one short time interval to another. By analogy, averaged over many time intervals, we expect each side of the particle to be hit by the same number of molecules. However, in any given time interval, one side of the particle may be hit by more water molecules than the opposite side (Figure 12.19(a)). The particle will experience a push in that direction. In the next time interval another side may get more hits than the side opposite to it (Figure 12.19(b)). What kind of motion will result from these irregular hits?

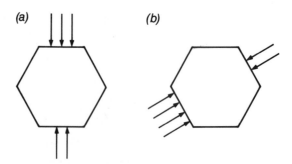

Figure 12.19
The "particle" being hit by water molecules. In each short time interval, a real particle is hit by many more molecules than those shown. a) During one short time interval, more molecules hit from above than from below. b) During a later short time interval, more molecules hit from the lower left than from the upper right.

12.7 "EXPERIMENT" RANDOM WALK

To see how random pushes might affect the motion of a particle, you can do the following experiment. A move of one unit in any one of six directions will be determined by the throw of a die. The numbers 1–6 on the die correspond to the directions shown on the hexagonal graph paper in Figure 12.20. For each throw of the die, you can mark the move on a sheet of hexagonal graph paper.

Using 12 dice on each throw will save you time. Notice that a "1" and a "4" cancel each other. The same is true for a "2" and a "5," and a "3" and a "6." Thus it is best, after each throw of the 12 dice, to remove the pairs "1" and "4," "2" and "5," and "3" and "6," and

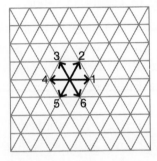

Figure 12.20
The directions on hexagonal graph paper corresponding to the number showing on the top face of a die.

trace lightly only the moves corresponding to the remaining numbers. Make about ten throws of the 12 dice and mark the positions of the "particle" at the end of each throw. Then connect these positions with a heavy straight line. An example is shown in Figure 12.21.

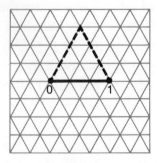

Figure 12.21
The motion resulting from the following throw of 12 dice: 2 ones, 3 twos, 1 three, 2 fours and 4 sixes. The 2 ones and 2 fours cancel; so do the 1 three and 1 of the sixes. This leaves 3 twos and 3 sixes.

Compare your results with those of your classmates.

- How would you describe the motion of the "particle"?

---

12 Prepare a cylinder like that of Figure 12.17(a), except that the lower layer will be a green nickel nitrate solution instead of the blue copper sulfate solution. On the basis of what you have read in this section:
a) Can you say what the final appearance of the cylinder will be after a long time?
b) Can you say whether the time it takes the cylinder to reach its final appearance is greater than, equal to, or less than 19 weeks?

13† At the instant shown, which way would the hexagon be pushed in Figure 12.19(a)? In Figure 12.19(b)?

14 Figure 12.21 shows the location of a "particle" after one throw of 12 dice. Can you predict where the "particle" will be after the next throw of 12 dice?

12.8   BROWNIAN MOTION

Solid dyes are often made of a colored powder. When the powder is mixed with water, particles of about 0.001 mm are suspended in the water. A drop of such a mixture can be placed on a microscope slide and then covered with a second microscope slide. This produces a thin layer of the mixture, which can be viewed through a microscope. When the mixture is dilute enough, only one particle at a time will be in the field of view. Connecting the microscope to a television camera and a television monitor enables us to follow a dye particle for several minutes (Figure 12.22). During this time the particle occasionally disappears, because it moves up or down toward either of the two glass slides and goes out of focus. When this happens, the focus knob on the microscope must be adjusted to bring the particle back into focus.

Figure 12.23 is a photograph of the monitor screen. The lower microscope slides had parallel lines marked in them. The lines are 0.05 mm apart. From this information you can estimate the size of the dye particle and the magnification.

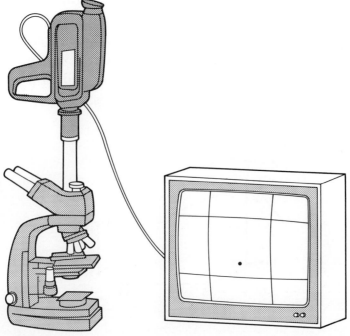

Figure 12.22
Apparatus for exhibiting Brownian motion. A television camera is mounted on a microscope and connected to a monitor.

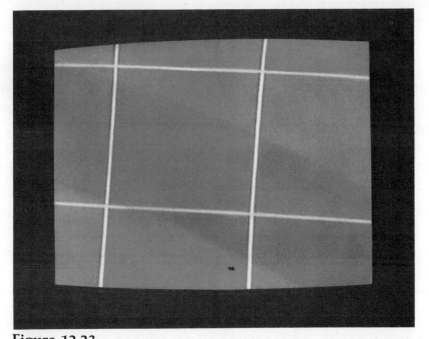

Figure 12.23
A photograph of the monitor screen. The lines shown are etched on the lower microscope slide and are 0.05 mm apart. These lines enable one to estimate the magnification and the size of the dye particle.

Marking the position of the particle on the screen at regular time intervals and connecting the marks by straight lines provided a record of the motion shown in Figure 12.24. The similarity between this record and the pictures you got in your "experiment" is striking. The tiny dye particles seem to move around as if pushed by the irregular motions of the water molecules.

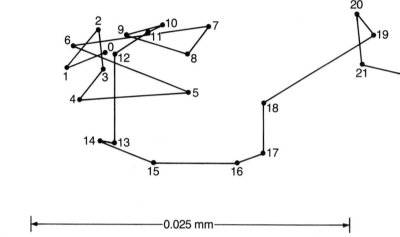

Figure 12.24

A record of the location of the dye particle at the end of time intervals of 16.7 seconds each. The particle seems to move around as if pushed by the irregular motions of water molecules.

The motion of the dye particles is called "Brownian motion," after the Scottish botanist Robert Brown. He was the first to observe such motion when, in 1827, he was looking through a microscope at particles contained in pollen suspended in water.

15 Why do you think that Brownian motion cannot be observed if the suspended particles are either too small or too large?

16 Suppose you have some smoke particles (about 10^{-3} mm in diameter) in a closed transparent container. You look at the smoke particles through a microscope. Would you expect to observe the Brownian motion of the smoke particles?

12.9 TEMPERATURE AND MOLECULAR SPEED

Let us return to the apparatus of section 12.2. What do we have to do to make the sphere gas expand under constant pressure, that is, without decreasing the load on the plastic disk? You might guess that if the spheres are made to move faster, they will strike the disk harder and more often. This will increase the pressure on the disk, and the disk will rise. As the disk rises, the spheres will have to travel longer distances between collisions with the disk. They will not strike it so frequently as before, and thus they will exert less pressure on it. Finally, the pressure exerted by the spheres will fall to just what it was before we increased the speed of the spheres. The disk will stop rising and will remain at the higher position: the volume of the gas will have increased.

In the sphere-gas machine, the speeds of the spheres depend on how fast the motor moves the platform up and down. By speeding up or slowing down the motor, we can change the speeds of the spheres. Figure 12.25 shows what happens when we have the motor running at different speeds. It is clear that as the speeds of the spheres increase, the volume increases. Since the volume of a gas increases with temperature, this behavior of the sphere gas suggests that the temperature of a real gas is related to the speeds of the molecules. At a higher temperature, the molecules move faster. At a lower temperature, they move more slowly.

To check this connection between temperature and molecular speed in a real gas, we have to find a way to speed up or slow down the gas molecules and see how the temperature of the gas changes. How can this be done?

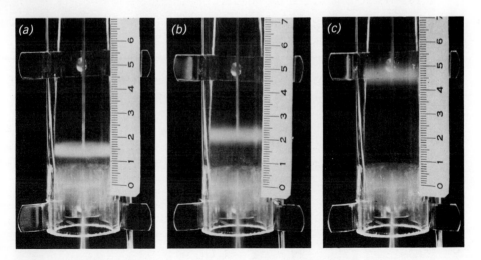

Figure 12.25
In each of the three photographs, the sphere-gas machine contains the same number of steel spheres, but the speed of the driving motor increases from (a) to (c).

When you throw a good tennis ball at a hard wall, it bounces back at practically the same speed at which it struck the wall. On the other hand, if you hit an oncoming tennis ball with a racket moving toward it, the ball bounces back at a higher speed than it had before the collision. If many tennis balls are hit by the moving racket, they will all bounce back at higher speeds; thus their average speed will increase by collision with the moving racket.

We may try the same trick with molecules of a gas. Instead of a tennis racket, we shall use a piston. Consider air in a tube closed at one end and fitted with a piston at the other end. While

Figure 12.26
A fire syringe. (*a*) Its parts are a protective metal outer tube, a glass inner tube with a wisp of cotton near its bottom, and a piston. (*b*) When the piston is pushed rapidly down the glass tube, the rising temperature of the gas ignites the cotton; (*c*) a flash of light is seen through the hole in the outer tube.

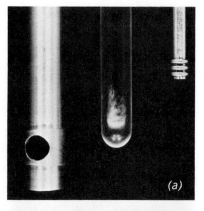
(a)

(b)

(c)

the piston is being pushed in, the molecules striking it will bounce back at higher speeds. In speeding up the molecules, the piston is acting like the moving tennis racket. Hence, when we compress a gas, we expect its temperature to rise. This effect can be demonstrated very convincingly by placing a little piece of cotton near the sealed end of the tube and moving the piston in with a quick push: the cotton will start burning, as shown in Figure 12.26. (Don't try this with a test tube. The tube will burst.)

To sum up, we have seen that the temperature of a gas is related to the average speed of its molecules. When the average speed of the molecules increases, the temperature rises.

In this discussion of the thermal expansion of a gas in terms of the atomic model, we have made use of only those two basic assumptions we used in the discussion of the compressibility of gases in the preceding section. These assumptions were (a) that the molecules of a gas are constantly in motion and (b) that the bouncing of one molecule off the wall of a container is not affected by the presence of other molecules. The assumptions do not depend on the kinds of molecules that make up the gas. Therefore, the atomic model predicts that at low pressures all gases have the same thermal expansion.

---

17 A fast-moving tennis ball strikes a racket that is moving back, away from the ball.

a) How does the speed of the ball before it hits the racket compare with the speed after it rebounds?

b) If the piston in Figure 12.26 is pulled up, what happens to the gas molecules when they rebound?

c) What will happen to the temperature of the gas as the piston rises?

18 Does a bicycle pump heat up when you pump up a tire?

19 How do you think the Brownian motion of a particle suspended in water at room temperature compares with that of a similar particle suspended in water near its boiling point?

20† The two liquids in Figure 12.17 were kept at room temperature during the diffusion. How would you expect the pictures to differ if the experiment had been run at a higher temperature?

12.10 THERMAL EXPANSION

The thermal expansion of gases is easily observed with the apparatus shown in Figure 12.27. When the glass tubes are placed in a water-filled container and heated, the mercury blob rises. From the change in height, the change in volume can be calculated. The results of the experiment are shown in Figure 12.28. Note that the points for all three gases lie close to the same straight line. Within the accuracy of the measurements, equal initial volumes of all three gases show the same increase in volume for the same temperature change, as predicted by the atomic model. Similar experiments have been made with many other gases. The results are the same as long as the gases are not too compressed.

Highly compressed gases have different thermal expansions, just as they have different compressibilities. We expect that different

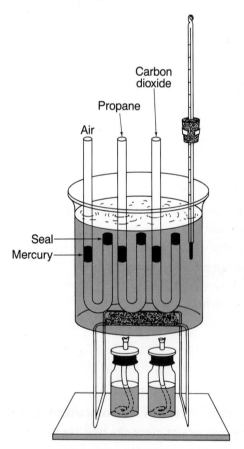

Figure 12.27
Apparatus for comparing the thermal expansion of gases. The tubes are bent to increase the volumes of the gases immersed in the water bath. The mercury drops are adjusted at the start so that the initial volumes of the gases are the same.

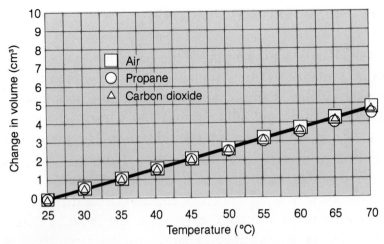

Figure 12.28
Graphs of the thermal expansion of three different gases that had the same initial volumes. The expansions are equal, independent of the kind of molecules.

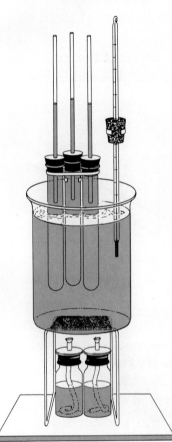

Figure 12.29
Apparatus for comparing the thermal expansion of liquids. The center test tube is supported by a clamp, and the other two are fastened to it by a rubber band. The height of liquid in each tube is adjusted before heating to equalize volumes.

liquids and solids will also have different thermal expansions. But when you warm up some water in a test tube, you do not notice a change in the volume. The thermal expansion of liquids is so small it must be amplified in order to be observed. This can be done with the apparatus shown in Figure 12.29. Consider one of the test tubes. Practically all the liquid is contained in the test tube, and only a small fraction is in the narrow glass tube. When the liquid expands, the small increase in volume of the liquid in the test tube pushes the liquid a relatively large distance up the narrow tube. Thus, the small volume change is amplified so that it can be measured. The results are shown in the graph in Figure 12.30. Clearly, the thermal expansion of a liquid depends on the substance. The same holds true for solids.

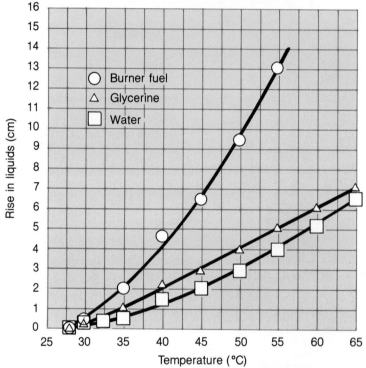

Figure 12.30
The thermal expansion of three liquids with the same initial volumes. The expansions are different, and depend on the kind of liquid.

These observations show that atoms and molecules behave in the simplest way when they are far apart, such as in a gas at low enough pressures. Under these conditions the change of pressure with volume and the change of volume with temperature depend on the number of molecules but not on their kind. In liquids and solids the kind of molecules makes a big difference. Evidently there is a need for a further extension of the atomic model of matter to account for these observations and predict new ones.

21 If the two tubes in Figure C contain the same liquid, and if the initial levels are the same, in which tube will the liquid rise higher as the temperature of the liquid in both tubes is raised equally?

Figure C
For problem 21

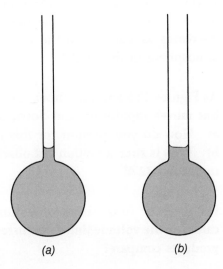

(a)   (b)

22 One of the liquids in the apparatus in Figure 12.29 has a volume of 33 cm³. Its tube has an internal diameter of only 0.3 cm and a volume of about 0.07 cm³ for each centimeter of its length. For a 10°C temperature rise for burner fuel, using this apparatus, the liquid rose 6.0 cm. What was the increase in volume per cubic centimeter?

For Home, Desk, and Lab

23 Bromine gas has a density of 6.5×10^{-3} g/cm³. Can this be the reason why the gas moves up through the air in the tube shown in Figure 12.1?

24 Figure 12.2 shows that when bromine vaporizes in a vacuum, the color seems to spread immediately throughout the tube. What does this tell you about the speed of the bromine molecules?

25 Would you expect an increase in pressure on the walls of the air-filled bromine tube in Figure 12.1 as the bromine evaporates? Why?

26 Do the moving steel balls exert any pressure on the side walls of the vertical tube of the sphere-gas machine? What changes would you make in the machine to check your answer?

27 If you run the sphere-gas machine with a long tube and without a top disk, the density of the gas is greatest near the bottom and decreases as you go up the tube. Is there a similar effect in the atmosphere of the earth?

28 As Figures 12.5 and 12.6 show, the top disk does not stay at one place but moves rapidly up and down about a certain average position.
a) How do you account for this motion?
b) Why is such a motion not observed in the experiment described in section 12.4?

29 For three or four values of volume and pressure in Figure 12.5, calculate the volume times the corresponding pressure. How do these products compare?

30 In terms of bricks, what is the approximate weight of the earth's atmosphere above the piston in Figure 12.13?

31 Try doing "Experiment" 12.7 with square graph paper, labeling the directions as shown in Figure D. Throw 12 dice 12 times and simply ignore any "5" or "6" that shows.
a) Which numbers do you pair this time?
b) Was the assumption of a hexagonal shape crucial to the main point of "Experiment" 12.7?

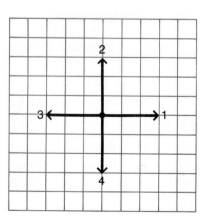

Figure D
For problem 31

32 In what different ways can you increase the pressure of a gas?

33 How is the volume of the steel-sphere gas affected by (a) motor speed, (b) number of spheres, and (c) the mass of the disk on top?

34 What two basic assumptions have we added to the atomic model developed in Chapter 8 in order to use it to describe the compressibility and thermal expansion of a gas?

35 Diesel engines do not ignite the fuel-air mixture with a spark from a spark plug as gasoline engines do. Instead, air in the cylinder is compressed by a piston. At maximum compression, fuel sprayed into the compressed air ignites and drives the piston back. How can you explain the ignition of the gas when there is no spark to ignite it?

36 a) Suppose the apparatus you saw in the film loop "How Does the Thermal Expansion of Gases Compare?" were used to study the properties of neon gas. How would you expect the experimental data to compare with those shown in Figure 12.28?
    b) Suppose the apparatus were used to study the properties of a mixture of propane and carbon dioxide. How would you expect the experimental data to compare with those shown in Figure 12.28?

37 a) If the liquid levels in the two tubes in Figure E are initially the same, will they be the same or different as the temperature of the liquids is lowered the same amount?
    b) If the liquids in the two tubes are different, can you directly compare their thermal expansion using these two tubes?

Figure E
For problem 37

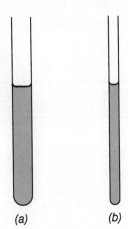

(a)   (b)

38   The following data were obtained using an apparatus similar to that in Figure 12.29, with water in one tube and air trapped by a drop of water in a second tube.

Temperature (°C)	Height of fluid in tube (cm)	
	air	water
23	0.0	0.0
25	3.9	0.4
27	7.8	0.8

What is the ratio of the change in the volume of air to the change in the volume of water for the same temperature change?

39   When heated, the glass in a thermometer bulb expands, as does the liquid that fills the bulb. Can you explain why the liquid in the tube does not go down to fill the larger volume of the bulb when the thermometer is heated?

40   Some bridges have one end firmly fixed to the support at that end of the bridge while the other end of the bridge simply rests on a roller. What do you think is the reason for this type of construction?

41   Houses are often heated by a hot-water system in which radiators and connecting pipes are completely filled with water. Such systems sometimes are connected to an open tank above the highest radiator. What do you think is the purpose of the tank?

42   Slip a thermometer into a one-hole rubber stopper, and measure its temperature. Remove the thermometer. Carefully holding the stopper with a pencil in one end of the hole, hammer the stopper rapidly and hard for a minute, and then measure the temperature. What do you observe? How do you explain it in terms of the atomic model?

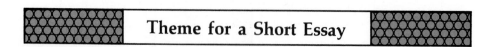

Theme for a Short Essay

Write a monologue entitled "A Minute in the Life of a Smoke Particle."

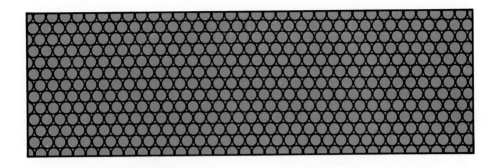

Epilogue

As this course comes to an end, you may ask yourself: "What have I learned this year in science?" We hope you will think of several things, some specific and some of a more general nature. Look back at the questions raised in Chapter 1. You still cannot answer some of these ("Is there a connection between brittleness and electrical conductivity?"). Others, which may have appeared equally perplexing ("What do you mean by a substance?") or even ridiculous ("When you heat something, does its temperature always rise?"), you can now answer based on your own experience in the laboratory.

The purpose of Chapter 1 was to get things started. In the chapters following, we tried to familiarize you with some of the basic facts and ideas of physical science. We showed you the evidence for the facts, and the usefulness of the ideas. Contrary to what you may have expected, science does not deal with absolute truths. The specific facts we find in the laboratory, such as masses, lengths, melting points, and solubilities, are all subject to the limitations of our measurements. Scientific laws, which are useful generalizations based on these measurements, also have their limitations.

If this is the case in science, whose methods require that we perform experiments under controlled conditions and repeat them many times to assure ourselves of the results, how careful must you be about the facts and generalizations you encounter in your daily life? Do you ask for evidence to support what you read and hear? If this introduction to science has made you a more critical reader, a more careful observer, and a sharper thinker, your work during the year was worthwhile.

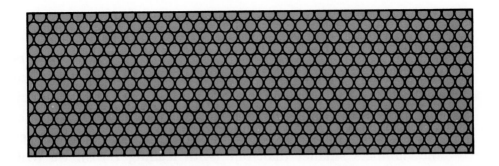

Appendix: Calculating in Scientific Notation

PART 1

SCIENTIFIC NOTATION

Scientific notation simplifies calculations made with large and small numbers by eliminating the need to use zeros as place-holders. Scientific notation thus enables us to write only the significant digits of a number. This appendix will help you to use scientific notation even if you did not study it in mathematics class.

Consider the shorthand notation introduced in Table 1.

Table 1

Written out	Numerals	Written shorthand	Spoken shorthand
million	1,000,000	10^6	"ten to the sixth"
hundred thousand	100,000	10^5	"ten to the fifth"
ten thousand	10,000	10^4	"ten to the fourth"
thousand	1,000	10^3	"ten to the third"
hundred	100	10^2	"ten squared"
ten	10	(10^1)	(shorthand not used)
one	1	(10^0)	(shorthand not used)
tenth	0.1	10^{-1}	"ten to the negative one"
hundredth	0.01	10^{-2}	"ten to the negative two"
thousandth	0.001	10^{-3}	"ten to the negative three"

The numbers in shorthand in Table 1 are called "powers of ten." The number at the top right of the "10" is called the "exponent." It is evident from Table 1 that the exponent of the number "10" equals the number of zeros in the regular notation. In order to distinguish between numbers larger than one (with trailing zeros) and numbers smaller than one (with leading zeros), we write a minus sign before the exponent for numbers smaller than one.

Any number can be broken up into a product of a number between 1 and 10, and a power of ten. The following examples show how this can be done.

$$3,000 = 3 \times 1,000 = 3 \times 10^3$$
$$3,200 = 3.2 \times 1,000 = 3.2 \times 10^3$$
$$0.05 = 5 \times 0.01 = 5 \times 10^{-2}$$
$$0.058 = 5.8 \times 0.01 = 5.8 \times 10^{-2}$$

The number multiplying the power of ten is called the "coefficient." A number which is written as a product of a coefficient between 1 and 10 and a power of ten is said to be written in "scientific notation."

You can think of the process of separating a number into a coefficient and a power of ten in the following way. Moving a decimal point three places to the left divides a number by 1,000, reducing 3,200, for example, to 3.2. To keep the value of the number unchanged, we have to multiply it by 1,000. Hence $3,200 = 3.2 \times 1,000$. (In 3,200, the decimal point is implied but not written.)

Moving a decimal point two places to the right multiplies a number by 100. To keep the number 0.058 unchanged after moving the decimal two places to the right, we must divide the new form— 5.8—by 100 or multiply it by one hundredth, that is, 0.01. Hence $0.058 = 5.8 \times 10^{-2}$.

---

1 Write the following numbers in shorthand:
   a) hundred million   c) ten-thousandth   e) ten-millionth
   b) billion   d) millionth   f) billionth

   Caution: For numbers smaller than one, always include the zero to the left of the decimal point: for example, 0.01, *not* .01. This will help to prevent mistakes in the shorthand.

2 Write the following numbers in regular notation and give their names.
   a) 10^7 b) 10^{10} c) 10^{-5} d) 10^{-7}

3 Write the following numbers in scientific notation:
   a) 8,000,000   d) 5,610
   b) 400,000   e) 423
   c) 370,000   f) 9,060

4 Write the following numbers in scientific notation:
   a) 0.6   d) 0.0506
   b) 0.07   e) 0.00042
   c) 0.004   f) 0.612

5 Write the following numbers in regular notation:
   a) 3×10^6 d) 8×10^{-5}
   b) 4.02×10^8 e) 7.2×10^{-3}
   c) 6.52×10^7 f) 4.07×10^{-4}

PART 2: MULTIPLYING AND DIVIDING NUMBERS IN SCIENTIFIC NOTATION

As a preparation for multiplying numbers in scientific notation, let us look first at products of powers of ten:

$$10^3 \times 10^2 = 1,000 \times 100 = 100,000 = 10^5$$
$$10^6 \times 10^{-4} = 1,000,000 \times 0.0001 = 100 = 10^2$$
$$10^1 \times 10^{-1} = 10 \times 0.1 = 1 = 10^0$$
$$10^{-2} \times 10^{-5} = 0.01 \times 0.00001 = 0.0000001 = 10^{-7}$$

You can work out other examples which will lead to the general rule: To multiply powers, we add the exponents (with their proper signs!). Thus, in the preceding examples, we could have arrived at the exponents of the products by addition:

$$3 + 2 = 5$$
$$6 + (-4) = 2$$
$$1 + (-1) = 0$$
$$(-2) + (-5) = -7$$

To multiply numbers in scientific notation, we can change the order of the factors in a product. For example:

$$(3 \times 10^5) \times (2 \times 10^4) = (3 \times 2) \times (10^5 \times 10^4) = 6 \times 10^9$$
$$(1.5 \times 10^{-2}) \times (3.0 \times 10^6) = (1.5 \times 3.0) \times (10^{-2} \times 10^6) = 4.5 \times 10^4$$

In general, to multiply two or more numbers in scientific notation, we multiply the coefficients and the powers of ten separately.

Since powers of ten are multiplied by adding their exponents, it is reasonable to expect that powers of ten are divided by subtracting their exponents. The following examples illustrate this rule.

$$\frac{10^7}{10^4} = \frac{10,000,000}{10,000} = 1,000 = 10^3 \qquad 7 - 4 = 3$$

$$\frac{10^{-2}}{10^3} = \frac{0.01}{1,000} = 0.00001 = 10^{-5} \qquad (-2) - 3 = -5$$

$$\frac{10^2}{10^{-2}} = \frac{100}{0.01} = 10,000 = 10^4 \qquad 2 - (-2) = 4$$

$$\frac{10^{-3}}{10^{-2}} = \frac{0.001}{0.01} = 0.1 = 10^{-1} \qquad (-3) - (-2) = -1$$

To divide numbers in scientific notation, we rearrange the numbers in a way similar to the one we used in multiplication.

$$\frac{6 \times 10^7}{2 \times 10^5} = \frac{6}{2} \times \frac{10^7}{10^5} = 3 \times 10^2$$

$$\frac{4.5 \times 10^{-2}}{1.5 \times 10^{-4}} = \frac{4.5}{1.5} \times \frac{10^{-2}}{10^{-4}} = 3.0 \times 10^2$$

In general, to divide numbers in scientific notation, we divide the coefficients and the powers of ten separately.

Note that the product or quotient of two numbers in scientific notation is not automatically given in scientific notation. For example,

$$5 \times 10^2 \times 7 \times 10^4 = 35 \times 10^6$$

Here the coefficient, 35, is not between 1 and 10. However, we can move the decimal point one place to the left, and compensate for this by multiplying the number by 10:

$$35 \times 10^6 = 3.5 \times 10 \times 10^6 = 3.5 \times 10^7$$

Here is another example:

$$\frac{4 \times 10^5}{8 \times 10^2} = 0.5 \times 10^3$$

To change the coefficient to a number between 1 and 10, in this case we move the decimal point one space to the right, and compensate for it by dividing by 10 (or multiplying by 10^{-1}):

$$0.5 \times 10^3 = 5 \times 10^{-1} \times 10^3 = 5 \times 10^2$$

6 Multiply the following numbers:
   a) $10^8 \times 10^6$ d) $10^{-3} \times 10^{-3}$
   b) $10^9 \times 10^{-5}$ e) $10^4 \times 10^{-7}$
   c) $10^{-2} \times 10^6$ f) $10^{-10} \times 10^{-12}$

7 Multiply the following numbers and express the results in scientific notation:
   a) $2 \times 10^7 \times 3 \times 10^{-4}$ d) $7 \times 10^3 \times 5 \times 10^{-2}$
   b) $4 \times 10^3 \times 4 \times 10^3$ e) $2.5 \times 10^4 \times 3 \times 10^5$
   c) $5 \times 10^{-2} \times 1 \times 10^{-6}$ f) $6 \times 10^7 \times 1.5 \times 10^8$

8 Divide the following numbers:
   a) $\dfrac{10^7}{10^3}$ d) $\dfrac{10^{-6}}{10^{-8}}$

   b) $\dfrac{10^4}{10^8}$ e) $\dfrac{10^{-4}}{10^3}$

   c) $\dfrac{10^{12}}{10^{-2}}$ f) $\dfrac{10^{-4}}{10^{-2}}$

9 Divide the following numbers and express the results in scientific notation:
   a) $\dfrac{6 \times 10^5}{4 \times 10^3}$ d) $\dfrac{2 \times 10^8}{8 \times 10^4}$

   b) $\dfrac{2 \times 10^7}{5 \times 10^{-8}}$ e) $\dfrac{3 \times 10^{-2}}{6 \times 10^4}$

   c) $\dfrac{7 \times 10^{-4}}{1 \times 10^{-6}}$ f) $\dfrac{7 \times 10^5}{2 \times 10^2}$

PART 3:   SIGNIFICANT DIGITS

Scientific notation eliminates the need for zeros as place-holders. It thereby removes any doubt about the significance of zeros in a measured number. For example, how many significant digits are there in 3,600 cm²? Is this measurement accurate to the nearest 100 cm², 10 cm², or 1 cm²? If regular notation is used, there is no way of telling. In scientific notation, however, it is generally agreed to write 3.6×10^3 cm² to indicate two significant digits, 3.60×10^3 cm² to indicate three significant digits, and 3.600×10^3 cm² to indicate four significant digits. Thus, we would use the last way of writing 3,600 cm² if the measurement of 3,600 cm² were reliable to 1 cm².

You are likely to use scientific notation mostly for calculations with measured numbers. You should therefore use the rule given in section 3.6 for the number of digits to be written out when multiplying or dividing the coefficients: The result should have as many digits as the measured number with the smallest number of digits.

10 Write the following measured numbers in scientific notation:
   a) 6,500 g to the nearest 100 g
   b) 6,500 g to the nearest 1 g
   c) 6,500 g to the nearest 0.1 g
   d) 200 cm³ to the nearest 1 cm³
   e) 5,040 cm³ to the nearest 10 cm³
   f) 70,000 cm³ to the nearest 1,000 cm³

11 What is the area of a rectangular piece of land with sides
   a) 3.5×10^3 m and 1.2×10^3 m?
   b) 6.3×10^2 m and 4.7×10^4 m?

12 Calculate the mass of 2.0×10^4 cm³ of oxygen. (See Table 3.1 for the density of oxygen.)

13 Suppose that a sample of a radioactive element has a mass of 3.2×10^{-3} g. It produces 4.5×10^4 helium atoms per minute. How many helium atoms would be produced by 1.00 g of the element in 60.0 minutes?

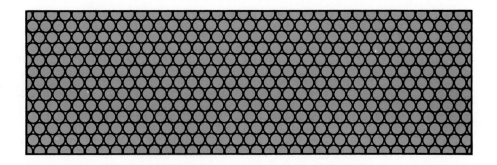

Answers to Problems Marked with a Dagger (†)

Chapter 2

1. (a) 8 cubes
   (b) 27 cubes
   (c) 8 cm³, 27 cm³
5. (a) 0.1 cm³
   (b) 0.2 cm³
9. (a) 10 cm³
   (b) 20 cm³
   (c) 20 cm³
   (d) 30 cm³
   (e) 0.60
14. 18.325 g
19. Boil away or evaporate the water. The mass of the salt recovered would be the same as at the beginning.
20. No
21. (a) 2.956 g
   (b) 0.054 g
   (c) About 2 percent

Chapter 3

2. (a) A
   (b) C
   (c) B
8. Measure the length, width, thickness, and mass of the rectangular blocks. Multiply length by width by thickness to get volume. Then divide the mass by the volume.
10. 1.7 g/cm³
12. (a) 10.5 g/cm³
   (b) 2.1 g/cm³
   (c) 0.82 g/cm³
15. (a) 0.50 g
   (b) 1.1 × 10⁻³ g/cm³
23. (a) 40 g
   (b) 50 g
24. (a) Gas
   (b) Solid
   (c) Solid or liquid
   (d) Solid or liquid
   (e) Gas

Chapter 4

10. From Figure 4.3: 47°C
12. From Figure 4.3: 212 g
15. The solids are not the same.
18. The solubility of oxygen in water decreases as the temperature of the water rises.
21. No

Chapter 5

1. They must have different boiling points.
7. They must differ greatly in solubility.
9. By distilling the seawater

Chapter 6

1. (a) Sodium chlorate and sodium chloride
   (b) By fractional crystallization
3. (a) 180 g
   (b) 180 g
4. No
6. (a) 18 cm^3
   (b) 2.4 $\times$ 10^4 cm^3
9. Tube I: 25 cm^3 hydrogen
   Tube II: 25 cm^3 oxygen
   Tube III: 0 cm^3
11. First package   Second package
    (a) 1.5   1.5
    (b) 0.6   0.6
13. Ratios: 2, 3, 4, 6, 7
15. (a) No (See Table 5.1.)
    (b) No, gasoline will vary from pump to pump.

Chapter 7

1. The solid has all the properties of copper; it is copper. Therefore, it would once again turn black and gain mass by combining with oxygen from the air.
10. Minerals in the soup or milk contain metals that give characteristic colors to the flame. Since sodium compounds are almost universally present in foods, the yellow color of the sodium flame is almost always observed in cases like this.
13. Y
15. (a) Nothing

(b) The sample remained the longest on the most intensely exposed area.
18. 33 readings

Chapter 8

1. It must suggest at least one new experiment and correctly predict the results.
5. No
9. 1,300 g
15. 1.5 = $^3\!/_2$
21. The formula for water is H$_2$O. Hence one mole of water molecules contains two moles of hydrogen atoms and one mole of oxygen atoms, and has a mass of $2 \times 1.01\,g + 1 \times 16.00\,g = \underline{18.02\,g}$.

Chapter 9

1. (a) Indirectly
   (b) Directly
   (c) Indirectly
   (d) Indirectly
4. (a) Yes
   (b) 1/1
9. 10 cm^3
12. The charges are equal.
15. (a) 20 ampere-seconds
    (b) 72 ampere-seconds
    (c) 72 ampere-seconds
18. The needle would gradually move to the right.

Chapter 10

1. The test tube in which hydrogen is collected.
11. One elementary charge.
13. So little charge would pass through the solution that no change in mass could be measured.

18. Connect an ammeter and battery in series between the two remaining connections. Connect the heater circuit. If the ammeter shows a current, then the positive end of the battery is connected to the plate terminal.

Chapter 11

2. 8×10^{-21} cm^3
3. 10^7 cm^2
5. 1.4×10^{-2} g
8. 10^{23}
10. 100 cm^3
12. 1.3×10^{18}. We assumed that the disintegration of one polo-nium atom produces one helium atom and one lead atom.
17. 2.2×10^{19} atoms

Chapter 12

3. The density will be doubled.
7. (a) $3P$
   (b) $\frac{4}{3}P$
10. (a) $2P$
   (b) $10P$
13. In Figure 12.19(a), downward. In Figure 12.19(b), toward the upper right.
20. Because of the increased molecular speed at higher temperatures, the diffusion would have been more advanced for the same time intervals.

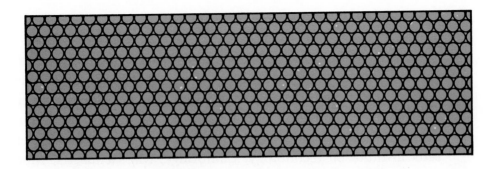

Acknowledgments

The following members of the Educational Services Incorporated staff in addition to myself were involved in the development of the course: John B. Coulter, on leave from Pakuranga College, Howick, New Zealand; Judson B. Cross; John H. Dodge; Robert W. Estin, on leave from Roosevelt University, Chicago, Illinois; Malcolm H. Forbes; Ervin H. Hoffart; Gerardo Melcher, on leave from the University of Chile, Santiago, Chile; Harold A. Pratt, on leave from Jefferson County Public Schools, Lakewood, Colorado; Louis E. Smith, on leave from San Diego State College, San Diego, California; Darrel W. Tomer, on leave from Hanford Union High School, Hanford, California; and James A. Walter.

For the summer of 1963, we were joined by Elmer L. Galley, Mott Program of the Flint Public Schools, Flint, Michigan; Edward A. Shore, The Putney School, Putney, Vermont; and Byron L. Youtz, Reed College, Portland, Oregon.

Later on, considerable time was devoted to this project by others who joined us during the summers or consulted on a part-time basis throughout the following years: Gilbert H. Daenzer, Lutheran High School Central, St. Louis, Missouri; Thomas J. Dillon, Concord-Carlisle High School, Concord, Massachusetts; Winslow Durgin, Xavier High School, Concord, Massachusetts; Alan Holden, Bell Telephone Laboratories, Murray Hill, New Jersey; Robert Gardner, Salisbury School, Salisbury, Connecticut; Father John Kerdiejus, S.J., Xavier High School, Concord, Massachusetts; Herman H. Kirkpatrick, Roosevelt High School, Des Moines, Iowa; Elisabeth Lincoln, Dana Hall School, Wellesley, Massachusetts; John V. Manuelian, Warren Junior High School, Newton, Massachusetts; John N. Meade, Newman Junior High School, Needham, Massachusetts; Paul Meunier, Marshfield High School, Marshfield, Massachusetts; Father Patrick Nowlan, O.S.A., Monsignor Bonner High School, Drexel Hill, Pennsylvania; Frank Oppenheimer, University of Colorado, Boulder, Colorado; Charles M. Shull, Jr., Colorado School of Mines, Golden, Colorado; Malcolm K. Smith, Massachusetts Institute of Technology, Cambridge, Massachusetts; Moddie D. Taylor, Howard University, Washington, D.C.; Carol A. Wallbank, Dighton-Rehoboth Regional High School, Rehoboth, Massachusetts; Richard Whitney, Roxbury Latin School, West Roxbury, Massachusetts; Marvin Williams, Bell Junior High School, Golden, Colorado; M. Kent Wilson, Tufts University, Medford, Massachusetts; and Carl Worster, Belmont Junior High School, Lakewood, Colorado.

I also wish to acknowledge the invaluable services of George D. Cope and Joan E. Hamblin in photography; R. Paul Larkin as art director for the preliminary edition; Barbara Griffin, Nancy Nelson, and Gertrude Rogers in organization of feedback from the pilot schools; Nathaniel C. Burwash and John W. DeRoy in apparatus construction and design; Benjamin T. Richards for production; and Andrea G. Julian for editorial assistance. Much of the administrative work was done by Geraldine Kline.

Throughout the entire project I benefited from the advice and criticism of M. Kent Wilson. Valuable assistance in coordinating various group efforts in the summers of 1963 and 1966 was provided by Byron L. Youtz. In editing this edition of the course, I was specially aided by Judson B. Cross and by Harold A. Pratt, who was responsible for the group summarizing the feedback.

I wish to thank the editorial and art staff of the Educational Book Division of Prentice-Hall, Inc., for their help in preparing the final form of this edition.

Constant sources of encouragement and constructive criticism were the pilot teachers, who voluntarily spent many extra hours relating to us their classroom experience. Without them, the course could not have been developed to this point.

The initial stage of the Introductory Physical Science Program was funded by Educational Services Incorporated. Since then, it has been supported by a grant from the National Science Foundation. This financial support is gratefully acknowledged.

Uri Haber-Schaim
March 1967

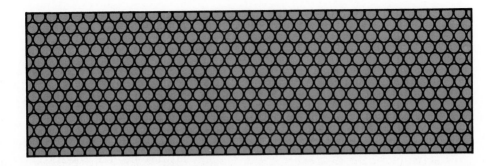

Index